THE OFFICIAL GUIDE

PENGUIN BOOKS

PENGUIN BOOKS

Published by the Penguin Group
Penguin Books Ltd, 80 Strand, London WC2R 0RL, England
Penguin Putnam Inc., 375 Hudson Street, New York, New York 10014, USA
Penguin Books Australia Ltd, Ringwood, Victoria, Australia
Penguin Books Canada Ltd, 10 Alcorn Avenue, Toronto, Ontario, Canada M4V 3B2
Penguin Books India (P) Ltd, 11 Community Centre, Panchsheel Park, New Delhi – 110 017, India
Penguin Books (NZ) Ltd, Cnr Rosedale and Airborne Roads, Albany, Auckland, New Zealand
Penguin Books (South Africa) (Pty) Ltd, 24 Sturdee Avenue, Rosebank 2196, South Africa

Penguin Books Ltd, Registered Offices: 80 Strand, London WC2R 0RL, England

www.penguin.com

First published 2001
1 3 5 7 9 10 8 6 4 2

Set in Bank Gothic

Made and printed in England by Butler & Tanner Ltd

British Library Cataloguing in Publication Data
A CIP catalogue record for this book is available from the British Library

ISBN 0–141–31321–8

ROBOT WARS™
EXTREME
™

THE
OFFICIAL
GUIDE

CONTENTS

Introduction

Robot technology is now so advanced that robots can be used to perform the most delicate and intricate tasks. It's possible to create a robot so sensitive that you could direct it to pluck an individual daisy from a lawn.

Forget that boring stuff! Let's see them fight!

Robot Wars equals guaranteed chaos and carnage as these awesome battle machines square up to one another in the arena with only one intent – to destroy their opponents. Only the best-equipped, most skillfully operated robots stand any chance of coming out in one piece. Weaker robots are bashed, smashed and trashed, hurled through the air or incinerated in a blast of flame. Only the strong survive... And only the strongest of the strong feature in Robot Wars Extreme.

Designed to test the talents of the roboteers to the limit and to pitch battle-hardened veteran robots against each other in the toughest contests they have ever faced, Robot Wars Extreme presents a whole new series of high-intensity battle scenarios.

All-Stars Tournament – Sixteen proven champions pitted against each other in a knockout competition that will provide fifteen unforgettably destructive battles.
Tag-Team Terror – Eight pairs of combatants are pitted against each other in seven battles that promise to be as destructive as they will be difficult to keep under control. Maximum carnage guaranteed.
Mayhem – Three robots lock horns in each of the twelve separate bouts. The winners then have the dubious honour of progressing to the Annihilator contests.

In addition to these main events, exciting new games such as the Challenge Belt, Wild Card Warriors and the People's Challenge will keep the action coming fast and furious. And of course, with all these battle-hardened veterans, there will be plenty of Vengeance Battles that will give those harbouring a grudge the chance to get their own back.

All this incredible action guarantees the most extreme robot battles ever seen. Not all the competitors will live to fight another day. A robot that's scheduled to do battle might be annihilated by its archenemy in an earlier event. This makes for mega-exciting, adrenaline-fuelled viewing – but it also means that some of the listings in this book may differ from what you see on the screen.

The Robot Wars Extreme Official Guide takes you through all of the competitions and profiles of all of the combatants. It also includes a bonus section on the World Championships. Every thing you need to keep track of what's going on from the moment you hear the first

3 ... 2 ... 1... ACTIVATE!

Rules of Engagement

The one single rule that dominates a Robot Wars battle is very simple – Kill Or Be Killed.

Robots

Like gladiators in a Roman arena, each robot is here for the sole purpose of fighting and winning. Every circuit, cog and gear is finely tuned for destruction. Strict technical criteria must be met in the construction of each robot to ensure it's battleworthy. However, the main guidelines are very simple.

- A robot must have full radio remote control.

- A failsafe must be fitted to immobilize a robot if remote control is lost in battle. This avoids the possibility of a damaged robot running out of control.

- Armour and weaponry are options to be chosen by the roboteers, but a robot may not be fitted with a projectile weapon.

- Robots must weigh no more than 100kg.

- A robot is expected to make every attempt to do battle for the full five minutes of each round.

House Robots

House Robots may only engage with a competing robot under two circumstances.

- When a combatant foolishly drives into or is shunted into a Corner Patrol Zone (CPZ), the House Robot patrolling that zone can attack. The attack can last up to fifteen seconds before the House Robot must disengage and return to its corner.

Damage inflicted by a House Robot in any such attack, including immobilization, is part of the battle scenario. Forcing an opponent into a House Robot's zone is, therefore, a very effective tactic.

- If a combatant is immobilized for more than thirty seconds, either by another competitor or a House Robot, the House Robots may close in to administer a 'mercy killing'. This will either involve the disabled robot being pushed into the pit or being flung through the air by the arena flipper.

THE JUDGES

A panel of three judges oversees the proceedings. Observing from outside the arena, they are there to make sure that the general Rules of Engagement are followed and to judge each robot's performance. The basic rules are as follows:

- Each round will last no longer than five minutes.

- Competitors must actively engage in combat during the five minutes.

- A win is declared when a robot has immobilized its opponent. Any robot that is unable to move for thirty continuous seconds is deemed immobile.

- If no robot has been immobilized after five minutes the judges will choose a winner based on points they have awarded each competitor in four categories: style, control, damage, aggression. Damage and aggression points will count most towards deciding who has won.

- When the judges declare a draw, the audience must choose the winner. The competitor that gains the most applause will win.

- Robots cannot win a bout by pinning their opponent to the floor of the arena. If a robot is pinned, the judges will order it to be released.

- Robots which grab hold of an opponent in order to bring their weapons to bear will be allowed to hold on to their prey for no longer than one minute.

- If the judges deem that two or more robots have become locked in a 'deadly embrace', they will order Ref Bot to separate the competitors. The clock may be stopped while the competitors are pulled apart and the round will then resume for the remainder of the five minutes. Alternatively, the round may be judged up to the point at which it was suspended.

MATILDA

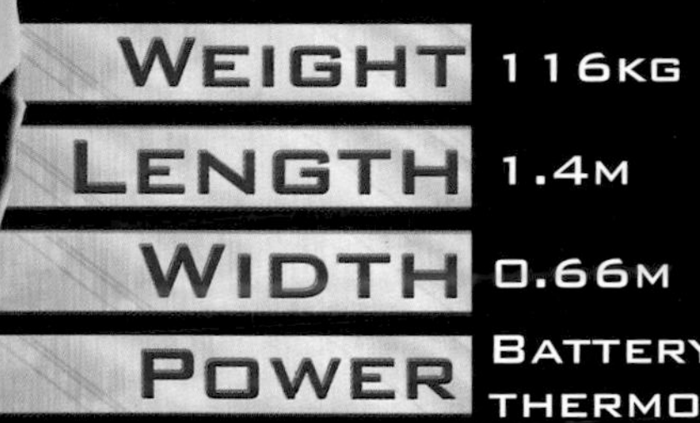

WEIGHT	116KG	0.66M	HEIGHT
LENGTH	1.4M	8 MPH	SPEED
WIDTH	0.66M		

POWER BATTERY-DRIVEN WITH THERMONUCLEAR STARTER MOTOR

WEAPONS HYDRAULIC TUSKS FOR LIFTING, SHUNTING OR PIERCING, AND A TAIL-MOUNTED CHAINSAW TO SLICE AND DICE. CHAINSAW IS INTERCHANGEABLE WITH A STATE-OF-THE-ART FLYWHEEL-WEAPON THAT WEIGHS OVER 25KG. THERE WILL BE NO WALTZING WITH THIS MATILDA!

SHUNT

Weight 105kg

Height 0.7m

Length 1.3m

Speed 10 mph

Width 1.1m

Power Prototype cold-fusion engine. Can drag a loaded Land Rover from a standing start to a speed of 6 mph

Weapons Diamond-edged axe hits with a force of 500kg per cm². Bulldozing shovels front and rear have been redesigned for extra strength, ensuring he'll be no pushover . . . as if!

DEAD METAL

WEIGHT	112KG	0.7M	HEIGHT
LENGTH	1.6M	12 MPH	SPEED
WIDTH	1M		
POWER	BATTERY-DRIVEN ENGINE WITH THERMONUCLEAR STARTER MOTOR		

WEAPONS 3000 RPM CIRCULAR SAW HAS BEEN REDESIGNED FOR ADDED DURABILITY. GRASPING CLAWS HAVE BEEN REBUILT FOR GREATER STRENGTH. YOU WOULDN'T WANT A HUG FROM THIS MONSTER!

Sgt Bash

Weight 120kg

Height 0.9m

Length 1.4m

Speed 5 mph

Width 0.9m

Power Powered by four massive batteries and a steam engine run on heat vented from the flame-throwing device

Weapons Turret-mounted flamethrower upgraded to super-barbecue power. Front pincer redesigned to become surgical steel jaws for added bite. Rear-mounted cutting disc means he can attack in any direction. Nobody messes around on Sgt Bash's parade ground!

Sir Killalot

Weight 280kg

Height 1.3m

Length 1.2m

Speed 8 mph

Width 1.2m

Power Combustion engine fuelled by petrol with hydraulic power to weapons. Drive-mechanism rebuilt to increase power to the tracks

Weapons Power lance on one arm and piercing jaws on the other. More than twice as heavy as any of the other House Robots and three times as heavy as the combatants. If you're hit by Sir Killalot, you really know about it!

Ref Bot

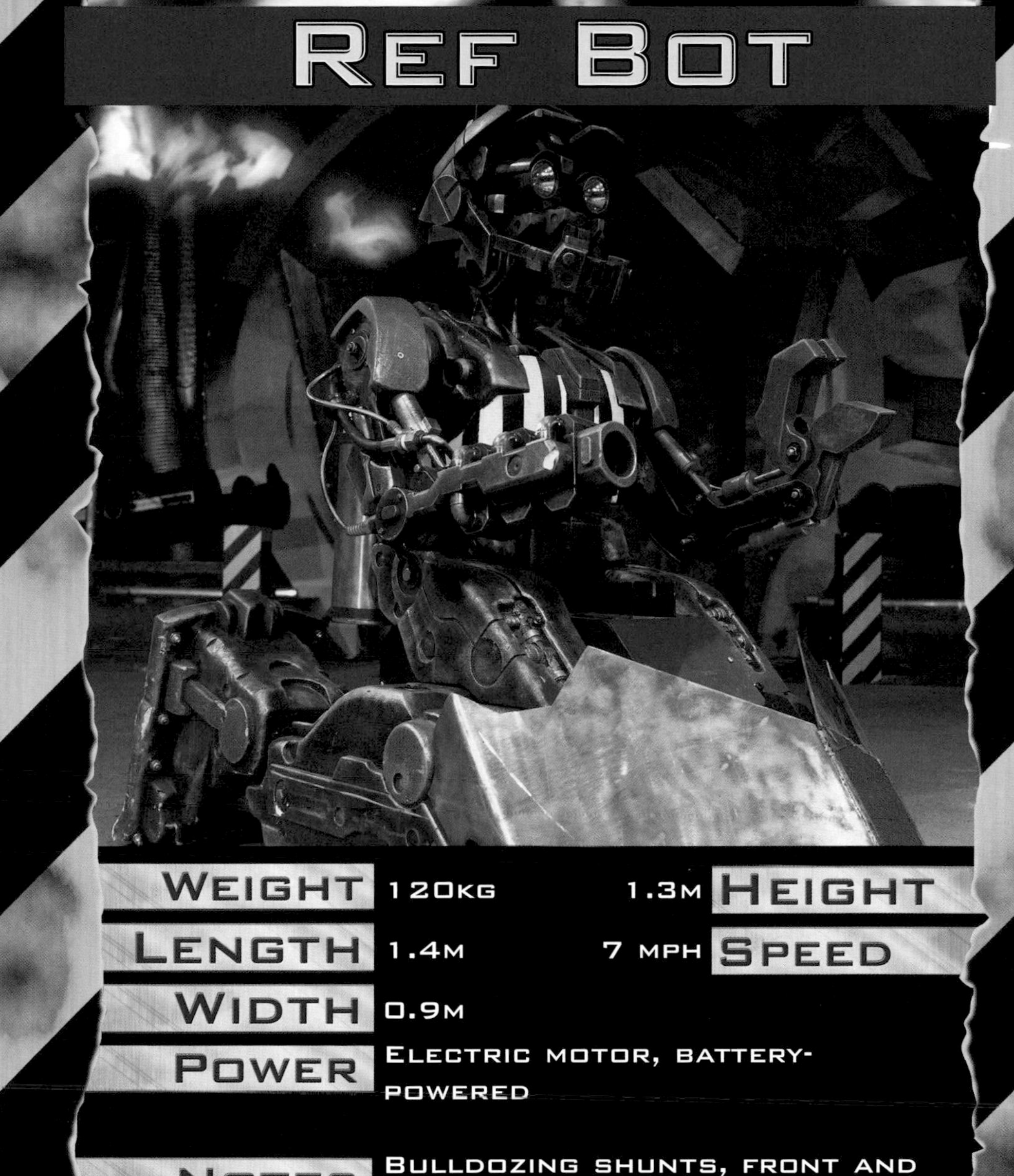

Weight	120kg	1.3m	Height
Length	1.4m	7 mph	Speed
Width	0.9m		
Power	Electric motor, battery-powered		

Notes Bulldozing shunts, front and rear, to separate robots that become locked in mortal combat. New electronic countdown board mounted on chest and light-indicator system on left arm. Pincer grip on left arm and fire extinguisher on the right

ALL-STARS TOURNAMENT

The All-Stars Tournament brings together sixteen of the most experienced, battle-hardened combat veterans in the world of Robot Wars. Their competition achievements include a list of Semi-Final placings as long as Sir Killalot's lance. There are finalists from all four previous wars and six championship or tournament winners, including the reigning World Champion, Razer.

RULES

Eight heats will narrow the sixteen contestants down to eight. These eight heat winners will be paired off in four Quarter-Finals, which will produce four winners, who will go through to the Semi-Finals. Just two will survive the Semi-Finals to battle for the All-Stars title in the Final.

So be prepared for fifteen of the most hard-fought, spectacular battles ever seen in a Robot Wars tournament. Every robot will have maximum opportunity to flex their muscles against opposition stronger than they have ever faced before. Reputations are at stake and there are a few old scores to settle. Expect maximum aggression in the grudge battles. Other competitors have gone through many wars without having met in the arena – will Behemoth and Diótóir finally get the chance to square up to each other? They'll have to make it through their heats first and then it's down to the luck of the draw.

Battle Board
Heats

Hypno-Disc	v	Behemoth
Chaos II	v	X-Terminator
Diótóir	v	Wheely Big Cheese
Panic Attack	v	Firestorm III
Wild Thing	v	Dominator 2
Tornado	v	3 Stegs to Heaven
Razer	v	Gemini
Pussycat	v	Stinger

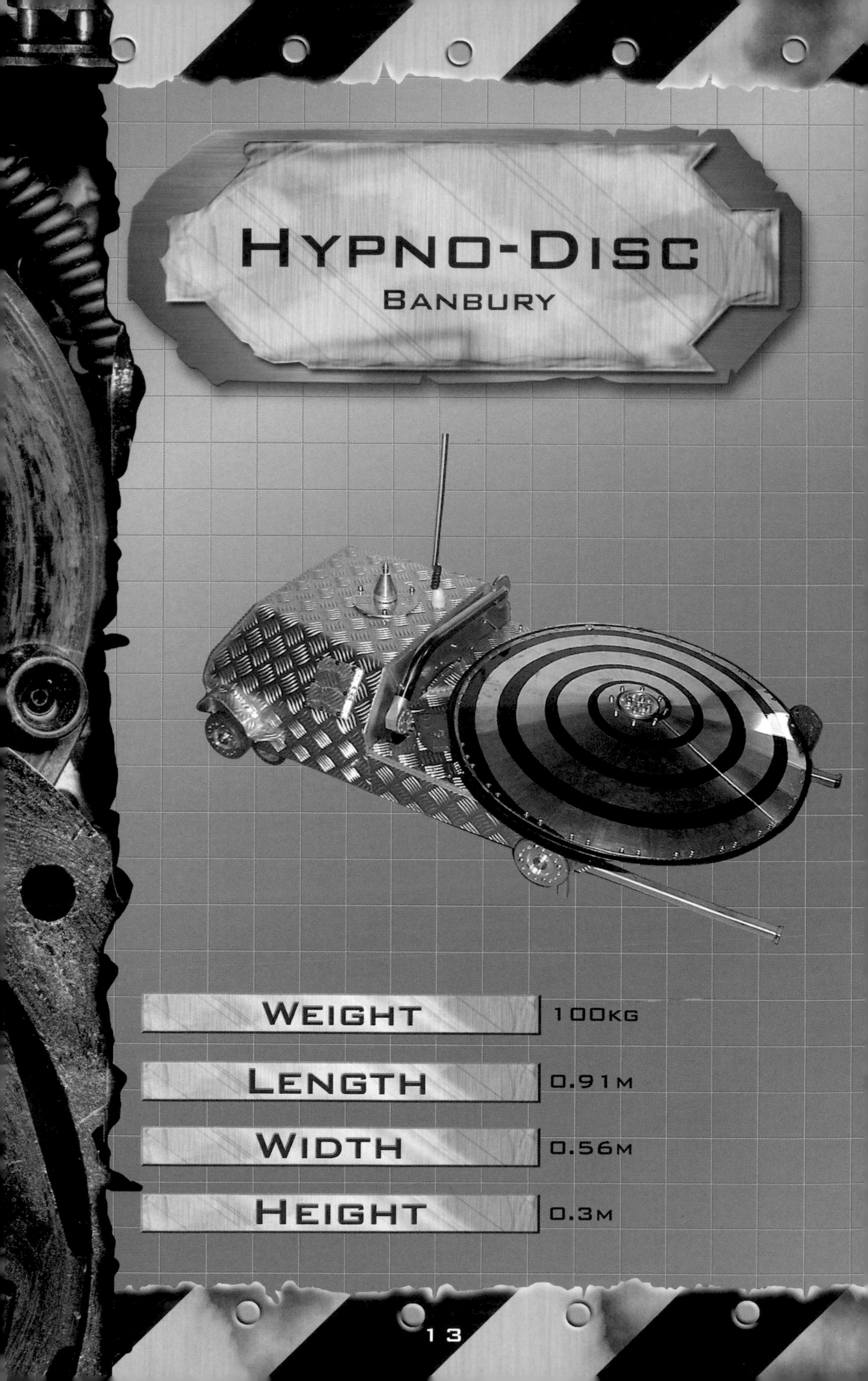

Hypno-Disc

Banbury

Weight	100kg
Length	0.91m
Width	0.56m
Height	0.3m

Speed
10 mph

Turning Circle
0

Clearance
25mm

Power
4 x 750-watt, 24v motors

Weapons
21kg two-toothed disc, upgraded from previous contests to spin at 850 rpm. Self-righting arm that has never yet been used in combat

Armour
Aluminium and steel plate

Team
Dave Rose (Captain)
Derek Rose and Ken Rose

Team Battle History
Series 3 Lost to Chaos 2 in hard-fought Grand Final when Chaos 2 flipped them
Series 4 Tore Splinter to pieces in Semi-Finals and beat Wild Thing on points before Pussycat, with a little help from Shunt's axe, knocked them out of the contest in the Grand Final

Notes
The Hypno-Disc team isn't afraid of anyone, although it does bother them that more manoeuvrable robots can try to keep out of range of their devastating disc weapon

BEHEMOTH

HEMEL HEMPSTEAD

WEIGHT	95KG
LENGTH	1.1M
WIDTH	0.62M
HEIGHT	0.57M

Speed

7.1 mph

Turning Circle

0

Clearance

25mm

Power

2 x 750-watt Bosch motors running through a custom-built chain-drive gearbox

Weapons

Pneumatic scoop that can lift 300kg. Axe to be added in near future

Armour

Titanium replaces the aluminium previously used on sides. Chassis redesigned to incorporate titanium

Team

Anthony Pritchard (Captain), Derek Pritchard and Kane Aston

Team Battle History

Series 2 Lost to Killertron in Semi-Finals when Killertron smashed open their shell with it's axe

Series 3 Attacked by House Robots in Heat Final. Were flipped, spiked and battered, but still running at 'cease'. Lost on points to Pit Bull

Series 4 Lost Heat Final to X-Terminator on Judges' Decision even though they flipped X-Terminator three times

Notes

The Behemoth team are nervous about coming up against Hypno-Disc (isn't everyone?) but they reckon they are more manoeuvrable than ever before and if they can only get their scoop under H-D, they might get their first opportunity to use that self-righting arm

Chaos II

Ipswich

Weight	83kg
Length	0.9m
Width	0.71m
Height	0.38m

Speed

12 mph

Turning Circle

0

Clearance

1mm

Power

2 x lawnmower motors

Weapons

Pneumatic flipper that can hurl a 5-litre oil can in the air. Larger CO2 capacity allows for more flips during battle. Flipper has been upgraded to titanium

Armour

Aluminium and polycarbonate

Team

George Francis (Captain), Ian Swann and Richard Swann

Team Battle History

Series 1 As Robot the Bruce. Showed enormous power, shunted Dead Metal and stranded Wedgehog on a grate to immobilize it in heats. Tipped over by Roadblock in Grand Final

Series 2 As Chaos. Reached Heat Final but beaten by Mace (now Gemini) after falling foul of House Robots – battered by Shunt and twice flipped by Matilda

Series 3 Narrow victory over The Big Cheese (now Wheely Big Cheese) in Heat Final before flipping Mace II in Semi-Finals. Flipped Firestorm in Finals before flipping Hypno-Disc to win the Championship and flipping Matilda and Shunt just for fun!

Series 4 Flipped Atomic ten times in Heat Final. Suffered battle damage to rear armour in titanic confrontation with Stinger in Grand Final, but won on points before being wounded again by Pussycat in Series decider. Fought back to win Judges' Decision and Championship

First World Championship – Beaten by Razer

Notes

One of Chaos II's closest calls came in a match against Stinger, where the judges announced that Chaos II had won by just one point. Beaten by Razer in the first World Championship, Chaos II are out for revenge

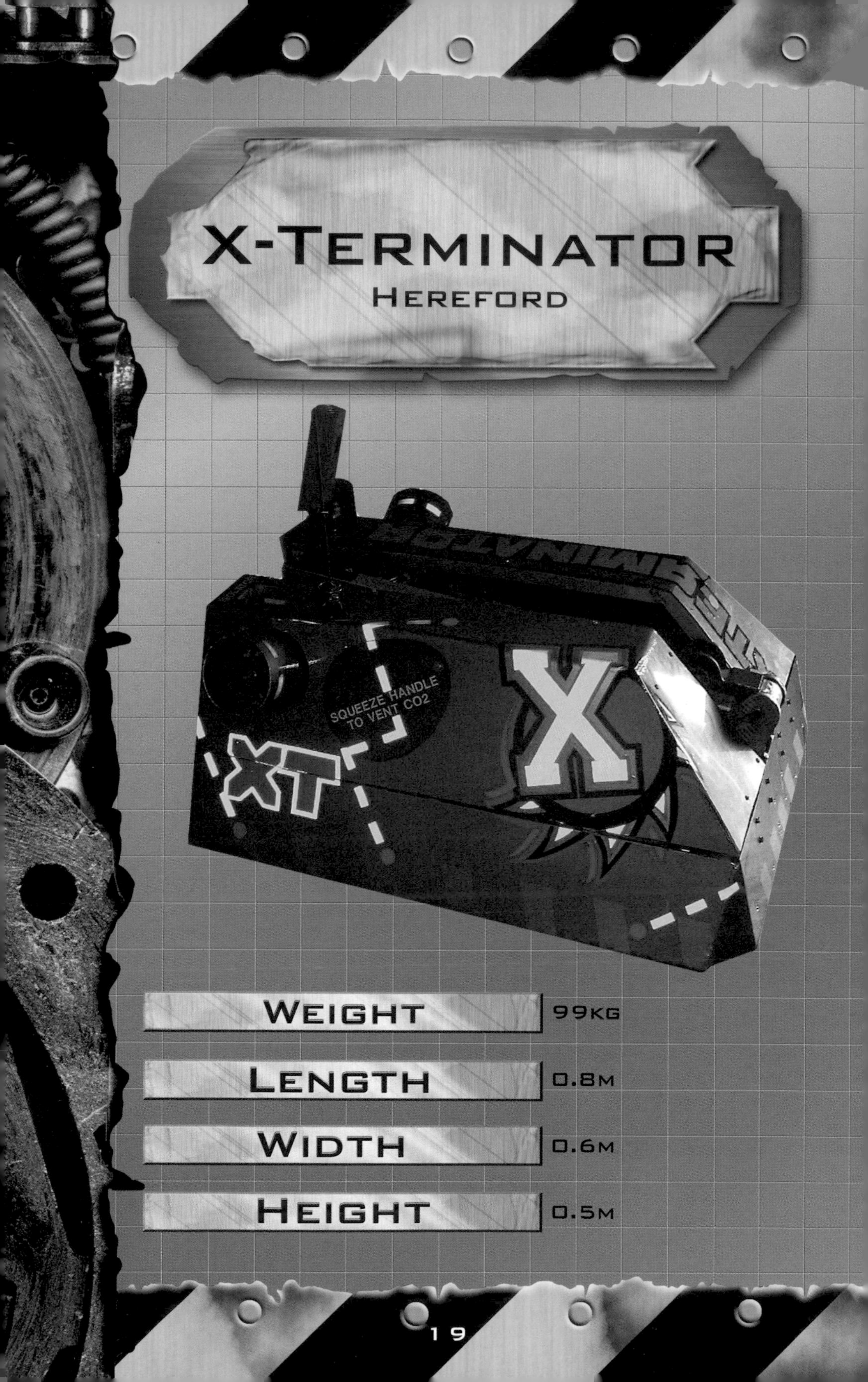
X-TERMINATOR
HEREFORD
SQUEEZE HANDLE
TO VENT CO2
XT
X
WEIGHT
99KG
LENGTH
0.8M
WIDTH
0.6M
HEIGHT
0.5M

Speed
9 mph

Turning Circle
0

Clearance
15mm

Power
2 x 750-watt Bosch motors

Weapons
Redesigned to incorporate more powerful axe and scooping shovel

Armour
Aluminium and polycarbonate

Team
Marlon Pritchard (Captain), Paul Lewis and Simon Baldwin

Team Battle History
Series 3 Did well against Panic Attack in Heat Final until damage to CO2 canisters caused weapon failure

Series 4 Points win over Behemoth led to an epic clash with Wild Thing in the Semi-Finals. Flipped by Wild Thing and, with its self-righting arm damaged, X-Terminator was terminated

Notes
The X-Terminator team most want to get to grips with Panic Attack who knocked them out of the Third Wars, but they'd settle for Chaos II as they just want to smash 'em up and put 'em in their place!

DIÓTÓIR
DUBLIN
WEIGHT
93KG
LENGTH
1.2M
WIDTH
1.07M
HEIGHT
0.95M
21

Speed

6 mph

Turning Circle

0

Clearance

0-2mm

Power

3 x 12v batteries

Weapons

Former flipping arm redesigned as more powerful crushing and flipping shovel

Armour

Aluminium and polycarbonate with fun fur cover

Team

Peter Redmond (Captain), Dr Zulu and Joe Gavin

Team Battle History

SERIES 1 As Nemesis. Fur set alight by Sgt Bash. Lost on points to Roadblock in Semi-Final after being attacked by all of the House Robots

SERIES 2 As Nemesis. After being set alight again by Sgt Bash in an early round, went into action in the Heat Semi-Final with a kebab attached ready for roasting, but ended up in the pit rather than the flames

SERIES 3 Sgt Bash managed to burn the fur again, but not before Diótóir beat Steel Avenger in heats. Firestorm pushed them in the pit in Heat Final to win

Series 4 Bolt From The Blue and Ming 2 pushed Diótóir over the flame pit causing the fur to catch fire yet again. Knocked out in first round heat

Sportsmanship Award – four time winner

Notes

The Diótóir crew are known as the nicest, most helpful, sportsman-like team in Robot Wars. The only machine they really want to mangle is Firestorm III, who knocked them out of the Third Robot Wars

WHEELY BIG CHEESE

SOMERSET

WEIGHT	100KG
LENGTH	1.43M
WIDTH	0.74M
HEIGHT	0.42M

Speed

6 mph

Turning Circle

0

Clearance

3.5mm

Power

2 x Formula 1 car batteries

Weapons

CO_2-powered pneumatic titanium flipper upgraded to lift a massive 800kg

Armour

Bulletproof titanium now thicker than ever

Team

Roger Plant (Captain), John McGugan and Murray Wharf

Team Battle History

Series 2 As The Mule. Lost to Plunderbird 2 on points in hard-fought Heat Final

Series 3 As The Big Cheese. Again reached the Heat Final, but lost to the all-conquering Chaos II, although they did manage to lift and inflict significant damage on Sgt Bash

Series 4 Flipped Killertron three times in a convincing heat win. Immobilized Suicidal Tendencies in the Heat Final but, in trying to shunt them into the pit, drove themselves into the pit instead. Won on a controversial Judges' Decision as Suicidal Tendencies was deemed immobile and therefore defeated. Lost on points to Tornado in a hyper-violent Semi-Final that left Wheely Big Cheese almost immobile and Tornado belching smoke

Notes

The Wheely Big Cheese team boast that they can flip a Mini Metro up in the air. They'd most like to get their cheesy snout underneath Hypno-Disc to show them they're not so tough or Sir Killalot to get their own back for past woundings!

PANIC ATTACK

IPSWICH

WEIGHT	98KG
LENGTH	1M
WIDTH	0.7M
HEIGHT	0.16M

Speed

7 mph

Turning Circle

0

Clearance

0mm

Power

2 x Truck windscreen wiper motors

Weapons

Electric lifting forks supplemented by top-mounted self-righting mechanism that can also grab an opponent and fend off blows

Armour

Aluminium and polycarbonate

Team

Kim Davies (Captain), Michael Davies and Christian Bridge

Team Battle History

SERIES 2 Beat Cassius to win Grand Final and become Series 2 Champions

SERIES 3 Slammed X-Terminator into arena wall to win Heat Final, but lost to Firestorm in Semi-Finals on Judges' Decision

SERIES 4 Picked up S.M.I.D.S.Y. and barbecued it over the flame pit before dropping it in to win Heat Final. Defeated Spawn of Scutter in first Semi-Final, but lost on points to Stinger in second Semi

Notes

Panic Attack have proved that they're among the toughest Robot Wars competitors ever – but X-Terminator still manages to get under their skin by claiming they could have beaten Panic Attack in Series 3 if their weaponry hadn't failed

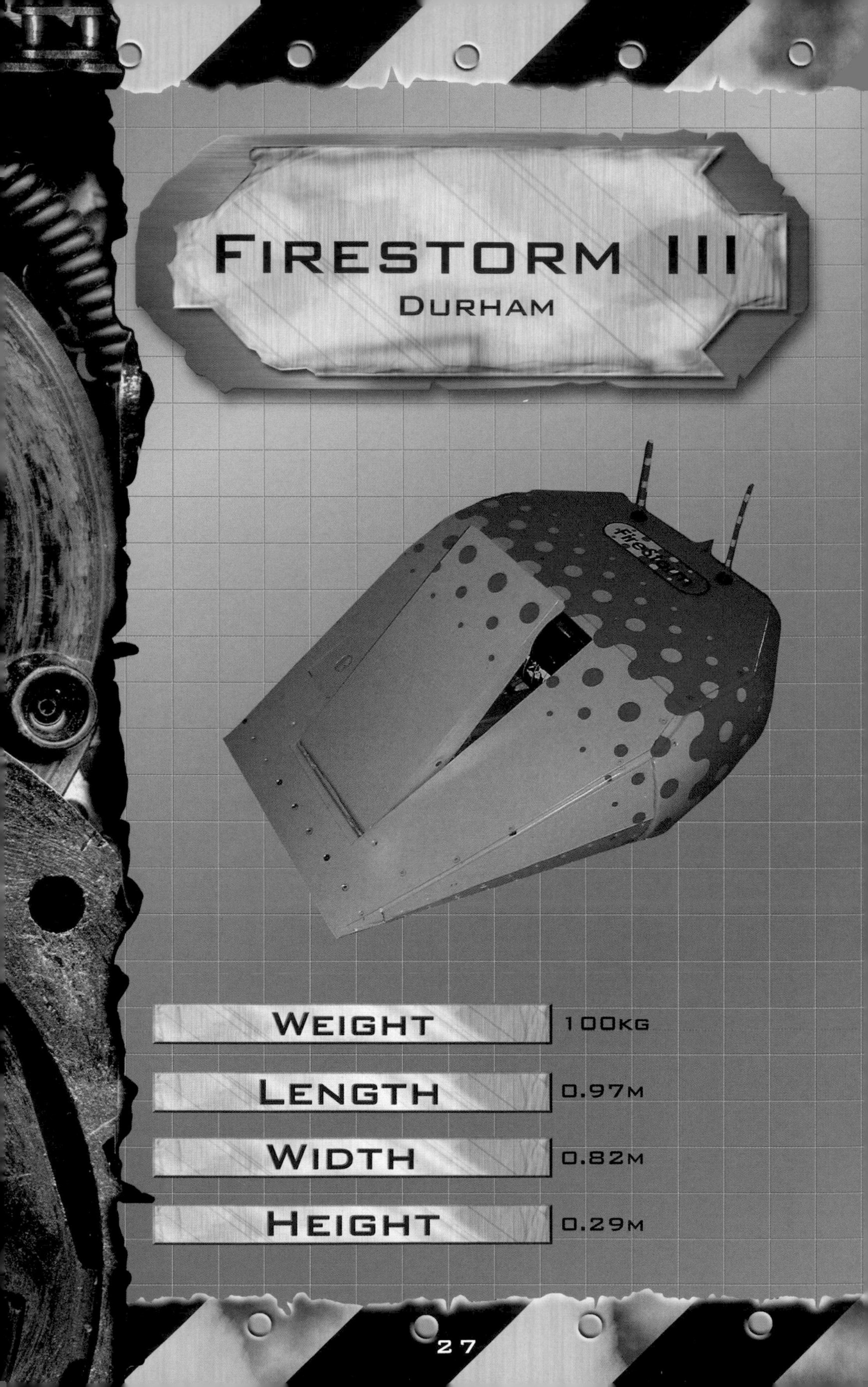

FIRESTORM III

DURHAM

WEIGHT	100KG
LENGTH	0.97M
WIDTH	0.82M
HEIGHT	0.29M

Speed
15 mph

Turning Circle
0

Clearance
1mm

Power
3 x 12v batteries

Weapons
Co2-fire-extinguisher-powered flipping arm. Rather than getting underneath an opponent and flipping them upwards, Firestorm aims to tip them over. Rebuilt with a faster action and 170kg lifting power

Armour
Aluminium increased from 3mm to 8mm after Dominator 2 punctured Firestorm II

Team
Graham Bone (Captain), Alex Mordue and Hazel Heslop

Team Battle History
Series 2 As Groundhog. Knocked out in heats, but still managed to topple Sir Killalot

Series 3 When Firestorm toasted Diótiór over the flame pit in the Heat Final, Dead Metal got a bit too close and also went up in flames. Beat Panic Attack on Judges' Decision in Semis but Chaos II was too strong for them in the Grand Final

Series 4 Beat The Morgue to win Heat Final on controversial Judges' Decision after they had driven themselves into the pit. Lost one of the closest battles ever against Dominator II in Semi-Final

Notes
Stripped down and totally rebuilt after the Fourth Robot Wars, Firestorm is desperate to have another go at Dominator after their encounter in the Fourth Wars when Firestorm lost on points

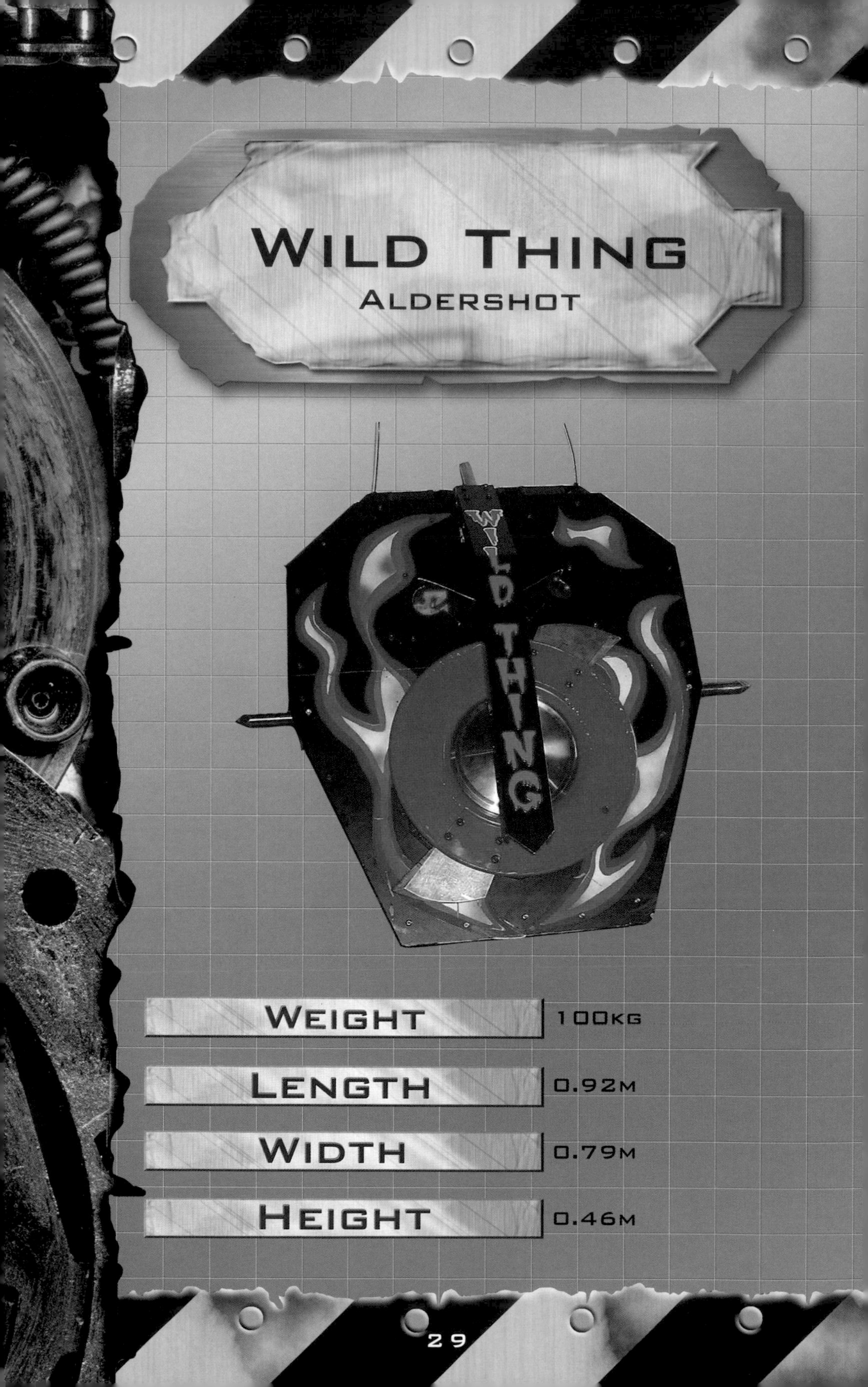

WILD THING

ALDERSHOT

WEIGHT	100KG
LENGTH	0.92M
WIDTH	0.79M
HEIGHT	0.46M

Speed
8 mph

Turning Circle
0

Clearance
0 mm

Power
2 x industrial electric motors

Weapons
The lance has been replaced with a two-blade, 10kg cutting disc mounted on the lifter arm. The disc is powered by its own Bosch 750-watt motor, and spins at 750 rpm

Armour
Aluminium and polycarbonate

Team
Nick Adams (Captain), Isabell Adams and Jake Adams

Team Battle History
SERIES 2 As Demon. Gave a spirited performance showing lots of promise but was knocked out in heats
SERIES 3 As Thing II. First gave Cerberus a grilling over the flames then managed to flip them to win Heat Final. Met Panic Attack in the Semi-Final who, with a bit of help from an arena spike, managed to flip them
SERIES 4 Beat Steel Avenger to win Heat Final and broke off Killalot's breastplate while defeating X-Terminator in Semis. Suffered battle damage to wheels in second round of Semis with Hypno-Disc and lost on Judges' Decision

Notes
Highly manoeuvrable on its go-kart wheels, the Wild Thing team is keen to test out their new weapon on Hypno-Disc or Panic Attack, both of whom they have lost to in the past. Their disc cuts low to disable wheels, but they're aware that exposed wheels are one of their weak spots too

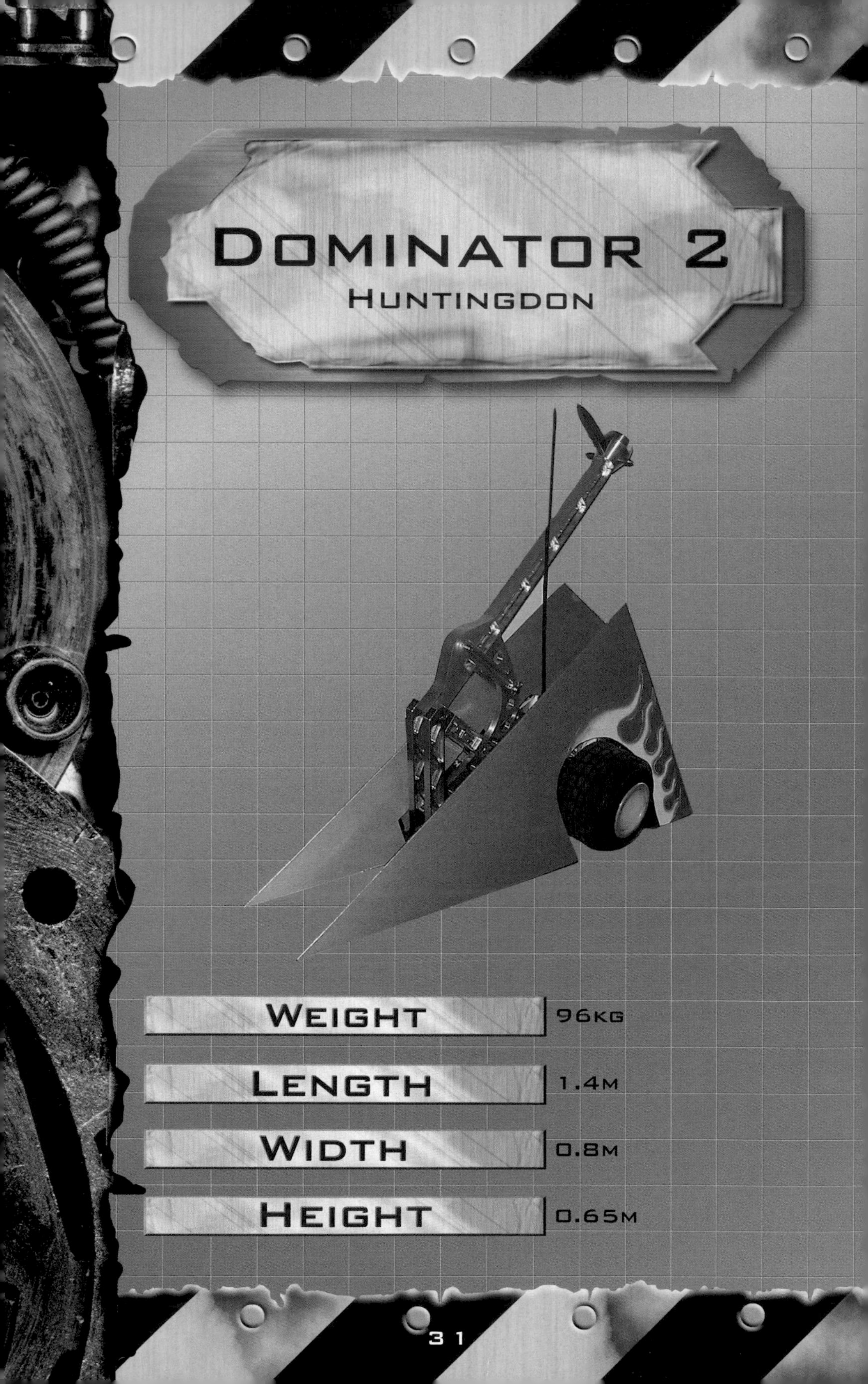

Dominator 2

Huntingdon

Weight	96kg
Length	1.4m
Width	0.8m
Height	0.65m

Speed

20 mph

Turning Circle

0

Clearance

10mm

Power

2 x 750-watt Bosch motors

Weapons

Pneumatic axe has been upgraded so it's heavier and more deadly than ever before

Armour

Plasma-nitride coated titanium increased from 1.8mm to 3.2mm

Team

Peter Halloway (Captain), Chris Hall and Elliott Smart

Team Battle History

Series 3 Came second to Razer in Pinball Tournament

Series 4 Beat Shadow of Napalm convincingly in the heats and 101 on points in Heat Final. Repeatedly flipped by Firestorm II in first semi-final – but self-righted each time, and plunged their axe into Firestorm's flipping blade to narrowly win on points. Came up against Pussycat in second Semi and started to lose their bodyshell in a ferocious battle which they finally lost on Judges' Decision

Notes

Dominator 2's new solid, treaded, go-kart competition tyres will only serve to enhance its reputation as a slick mover. The thicker angled armour should deflect blows better than ever before. Pussycat had better watch out as Dominator 2 is out for revenge after their defeat on points in the Fourth Wars

TORNADO

HUNTINGDON

WEIGHT	97KG
LENGTH	0.9M
WIDTH	0.75M
HEIGHT	0.25M

Speed
10 mph

Turning Circle
0

Clearance
5mm

Power
2 x 750-watt Bosch motors

Weapons
New pointed front end to aid shunting. Rear end houses ramming spikes and a 7kg, two-toothed, 2500 rpm cutting disc powered by its own Bosch motor. The disc replaces the old pneumatic spike

Armour
Steel and polycarbonate. Titanium added to protect battery housings as Shunt managed to damage a battery during the Fourth Wars

Team
Andrew Marchant (Captain), David Gamble and Bryan Moss

Team Battle History
Series 4 Beat Gemini in Heat final by impaling one of the bots on an arena wall spike and fighting off the other bot as it tried to rescue its twin. Then faced Wheely Big Cheese in a hard-fought Semi. Thrown twice in the air, Tornado still managed to inflict loads of damage and was smoking badly when the judges awarded it the match. Lost to Chaos II in second Semi-Final when they were flipped out of the arena

Notes
While their four-wheel drive, flat and low configuration means they can run either way up and don't care about being flipped, Tornado are wary of coming up against crushers like Razer because they know how vulnerable they are to those sorts of weapons. The cutting disc has been added to give them the extra bite they felt was lacking in their old pneumatic spike

3 Stegs to Heaven

Southampton

Weight	72kg
Length	0.85m
Width	0.7m
Height	0.35m

Speed

15 mph

Turning Circle

0

Clearance

5mm

Power

2 x 750-watt Bosch motors, one driving each wheel

Weapons

Completely redesigned from Steg 2, 3 Stegs has a rounded nose at one end for shunting, and a twin-blade revolving cutter at the other

Armour

4.5mm thick steel plate

Team

Peter Rowe (Captain), Danny King and Richard Francis

Team Battle History

Series 3 As Steg-O-Saw-Us. Rammed, bent and bashed Napalm to win Heat Final, then beat Gravedigger and The Beast of Bodmin to win a place in the Grand Final. Lost to Hypno-Disc, who managed to break one of Steg's tracks

Series 4 As Steg 2. Flipped and pushed Mortis into the pit to win Heat Final. Fought Chaos II in Semi-Final – they flipped each other all over the arena until Steg 2 landed on its side and was immobilized

Notes

3 Stegs to Heaven are ready to take on anybody, especially Chaos II because they have a score to settle from the Fourth Wars

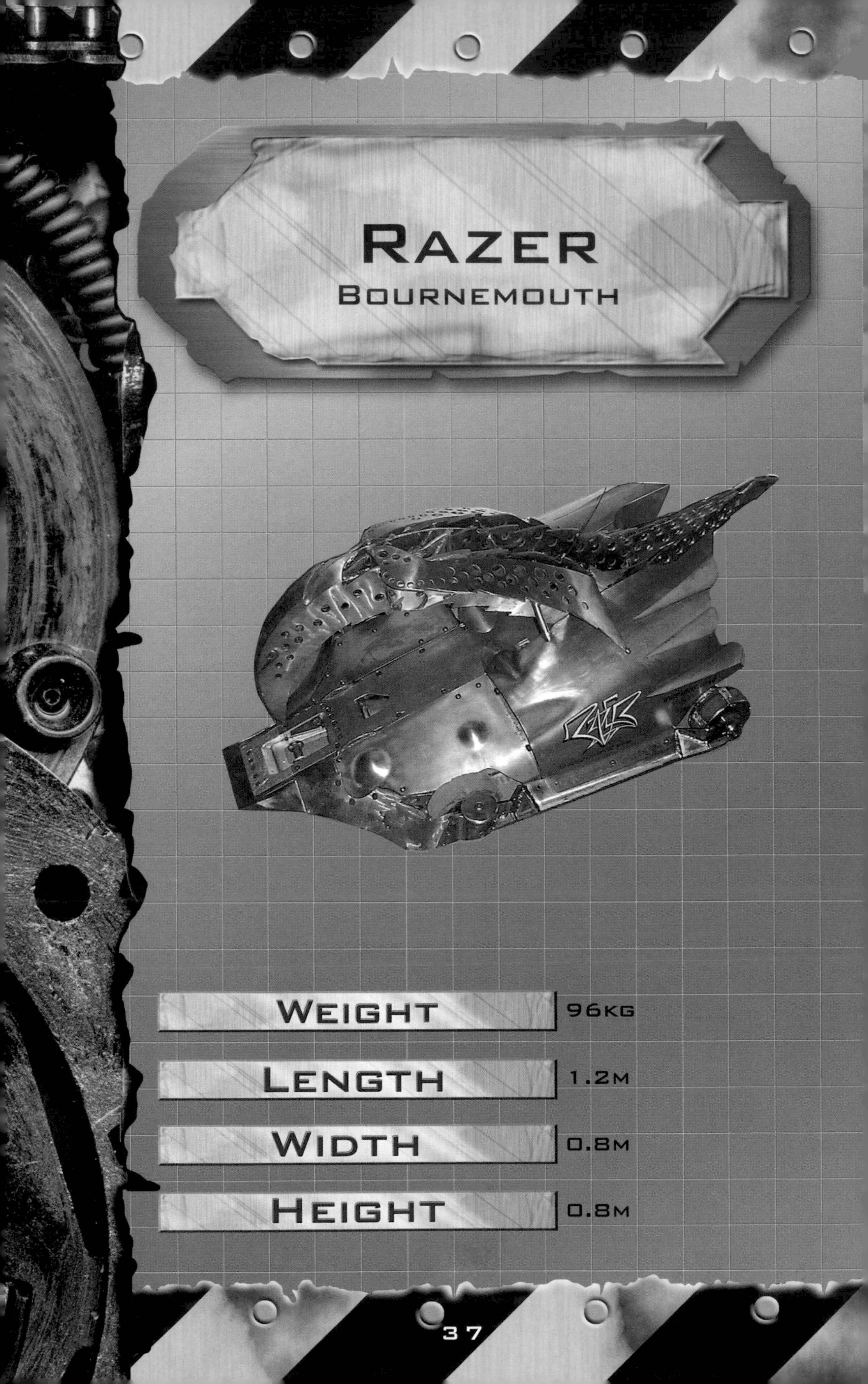

RAZER
BOURNEMOUTH

WEIGHT	96KG
LENGTH	1.2M
WIDTH	0.8M
HEIGHT	0.8M

Speed

11 mph

Turning Circle

0

Clearance

1-8mm

Power

2 x 12v golf caddy electric motors

Weapons

Hydraulic piercer powered by a ram from a truck tail lift, bears down on an opponent with a pressure of 9 tonnes. Tipped with stainless steel

Armour

Titanium and 2.5mm case-hardened steel, rounded or angled so that saws should just skid off

Team

Simon Scott (Captain), Ian Lewis and Vincent Blood

Team Battle History

Series 2 Suffered mechanical failure in heats after showing off their destructive power on Inquisitor and even shunting Shunt

Series 3 Razer had a convincing first heat win against Backstabber before losing control of its self-righting mechanism which left it unable to manoeuvre in the match against Aggrobot. Winners of the Pinball Tournament

Series 4 Decimated Milly Ann Bug in heats before meeting Pussycat in the Heat Final only to suffer mechanical failure yet again. Winners of the Annihilator (South)

Winners of the first World Championship

Reigning World and International Champion

Best design award Series 2 and Series 3

Notes

Razer reckons that the robot they should fear most is Razer itself! They have suffered three breakdowns in a row in UK competitions. Only Chaos II has ever beaten them outright and that was in a non-championship event. They also owe Pussycat a thrashing after the team wore bits of Razer round their necks as souvenirs after their last confrontation

GEMINI

HASTINGS

WEIGHT	94KG
LENGTH	0.74M
WIDTH	0.7M
HEIGHT	0.38M

Speed

5-6 mph

Turning Circle

0

Clearance

15mm

Power

4 x wheelchair motors, driving wheels now with solid tyres to avoid the puncture suffered during the Fourth Wars

Weapons

Each of the two halves of this cluster bot is armed with a pneumatic flipper. The flipper arms have been strengthened and can lift in excess of 250kg

Armour

Fibreglass and kevlar armour now thicker than ever. Lightweight shell allows two-in-one robot to be built within weight restrictions

Team

Shane Howard, Brian Fountain and Daryl Howard

Team Battle History

Series 2 As Mace. Helped Matilda spike Chaos during heats, but then got to know the pit quite well as they ended up there twice during Semi-Final Gauntlet trial

Series 3 As Mace II. Beat Stinger and Suicidal Tendencies to win their heat and flipped Big Brother for Sgt Bash to finish them off in first Semi. In a re-run of their Series 2 clash, they faced Chaos II in a gargantuan battle in the second Semi, but were defeated when flipped and immobilized

Series 4 The cluster bots worked perfectly when they ganged up on The Creature in their first heat but Tornado proved too much for them in the Heat Final. Winners of the Pinball Tournament

Notes

Nobody thought that a cluster bot could be built within the Robot Wars weight limits, but the Gemini team proved them wrong. Now they are the only robot warriors who can surround their enemy

Pussycat

Gloucester

Weight	97kg
Length	0.56m
Width	0.74m
Height	0.97m

Speed
15 mph

Turning Circle
0

Clearance
40mm

Power
2 x 750-watt Bosch motors

Weapons
Upgraded, thicker and heavier two-toothed circular spinning blade. Powered by separate motor and battery

Armour
Aluminium and polycarbonate side plates now much thicker at 13mm instead of 6mm

Team
Alan Gribble (Captain), David Gribble and Robert Bettington

Team Battle History
SERIES 1 As Bodyhammer. Beat Torque of the Devil and Reali-T to reach Grand Final where they lost on points to Roadblock
SERIES 2 As Bodyhammer. Knocked out during trials by Sir Killalot
SERIES 3 Disposed of Hammerhead and Cassius II, putting them into the pit during Heats. Faced Scutter's Revenge in Heat Final and during the bout, Pussycat's blade shattered. Hardened blades, liable to shatter, are against technical regulations, so Pussycat was disqualified, losing even though Scutter's Revenge were in flames!
SERIES 4 Defeated Razer in Heat Final and sliced through Thermidor's armour to win on points in the first Semi. Had a go at Dominator 2's wheels before dislodging its bodyshell to win second Semi on points. Badly damaged Hypno-Disc in first round of the Grand Final, but were almost flipped out of the arena by Chaos II in series decider and lost the Judges' Decision

Notes
Pussycat has a formidable reputation in combat. Its four-wheel drive means it can run upright or horizontally forwards and backwards. Being tipped sideways was a potential problem until the addition of special side wheel grips that will now right it from any position

Stinger

Lincolnshire

Weight	83kg
Length	0.71m
Width	0.61m
Height	0.38m

Speed

8 mph

Turning Circle

0

Clearance

0

Power

2 x 750-watt Bosch motors

Weapons

Heavier, more-powerful axe/spike. Extra strengthening on arm also acts as blade weapon

Armour

Steel shell with Kevlar-reinforced tyres

Team

Kevin Scott (Captain), Karl Skinner and Tim Mann

Team Battle History

SERIES 3 Unlucky to lose to Mace II in heats, where they attacked aggressively but ended up in the pit

SERIES 4 Beat Bulldog Breed II in Heat Final, piercing their armour and disabling their weapon. Went on to beat Mousetrap in first Semi and pounded Panic Attack with a barrage of blows in second Semi to win on points. Unlucky to lose the Judges' Decision in their Grand-Final bout with Chaos II after ripping off a chunk of Chaos II's armour and landing some stunning hits

Notes

Everything about Stinger is designed to give more weight to that mighty axe. Even the batteries swing round to add their weight and a special 3kg sliding weight inside the shaft also pitches in. All of that is bad news for Chaos II, who are top of Stinger's hit list after knocking Stinger out of the Fourth Wars in a Semi-Final that Stinger controversially claims was fixed!

In the Battle

The robots themselves are the true warriors of Robot Wars, providing gut-wrenching, awe-inspiring displays of spectacular action. However, the arena itself also plays a part in the battle. There's the arena Flipper waiting to help provide a mercy-killing by hurling an immobilized warrior through the air. Jets of CO2 shooting from the floor can obscure a close-quarter clinch for a vital split second and sheets of flame can turn a battle into a barbecue.

Zone

Then there's the arena's own spinning cutter and, of course, the pit. Any robot dumped or pushed into the pit is deemed dead and the bout is over. And with the battle-happy audience often shouting for a failing robot to be put out of its misery and dumped in the pit, the House Robots are only too happy to oblige.

The audience is protected from the flying debris of disintegrating robots by the arena walls which are made of transparent bullet-proof polycarbonate. No humans may enter the arena while any of the robots are still activated. But then, who on earth would want to?

TAG-TEAM TERROR

The Tag-Team format is quite simple, but promises to provide some of the most ferocious confrontations ever witnessed on Robot Wars.

RULES

Two teams of two robots enter the arena. Only one robot from each team may engage the enemy at any time. If a robot wishes to disengage and give its partner a piece of the action, it must return to its corner and 'tag' its partner. The two robots then swap places.

That's the theory, anyway, but few roboteers can bear to hang around in their corner while their partner is having the circuitry knocked out of them. Turning the bout into a free-for-all is, naturally, strongly discouraged, but it's great to watch!

Eight tag teams contest four heats with the four heat winners progressing to two Semi-Finals. The winners of each of the Semi-Finals then battle it out in the Final to decide the Tag-Team Terror Championship.

Battle Board
Heats

King B Powerworks + 101
v
Diótiór + Mega morg

Major Tom + Bigger Brother
v
Comengetorix + Spawn Again

Napalm + Sir Chromalot
v
Steel Avenger + Suicidal Tendencies

Cerberus + Thermidor II
v
S.M.I.D.S.Y. + Sumpthing

King B Powerworks

Portsmouth

Weight	88kg
Length	1m
Width	0.77m
Height	0.25m

Speed

20 mph

Turning Circle

0

Clearance

50 mm

Power

2 x 750-watt 36v motors

Weapons

Electric lifting and ramming spikes tipped with Hilti chisel blades. Rear-mounted two-toothed cutter, powered by separate motor and revolving at 8000 rpm

Armour

Steel and polycarbonate

Team

Simon Harrison (captain) and Grant Hornsby

Team Battle History

Series 2 As King Buxton. Beat RoboDoc (now 101) in Heat Semi on Judges' Decision. Then pushed All Torque (now Fighting Torque) into the pit to win Heat Final. They were torched by Sgt Bash in the Semi-Final and eventually slain by Roadblock's circular saw

Series 3 As King Buxton. Defeated Eric in an edge-of-the-pit encounter, then immobilized Weld-Dor with their ramming spikes in second heat. Came up against the RoboDoc team again in the Heat Final when they were axed by Shunt and ended the bout in a cloud of smoke with 101 declared winner

Series 4 As King B3. Squared up to Atomic for a shunting match in second-round heat, but they were flipped and battered until they caught fire and were eliminated. Winners of Series 4 Tag-Team contest with 101

Notes

Despite being totally rebuilt at a cost of over £4,000, King B Powerworks still looks much the same as the old King B3. they're still smarting from being defeated by 101 in the Third Wars Heat Final. Once the Tag-Team contest is over, there's no telling what might happen!

101
Kettering

Weight	97kg
Length	1.2m
Width	0.75m
Height	0.3m

Speed

8 mph

Turning Circle

0

Clearance

50mm

Power

2 x ISKRA industrial electric motors powered by racing car batteries

Weapons

Ramming/stabbing spike. Proximity-sensors revised to sense whether spike has penetrated enemy and repeat 200 mph thrusting action until successful

Armour

Aircraft-grade aluminium

Team

Mike Franklin (Captain), Amy Franklin and Steve Bickle

Team Battle History

Series 2 As RoboDoc. Ran rampant in the heat trials where they were flipped by Matilda. In the thick of the battle Sgt Bash set light to Sir Killalot. Eventually lost in heats to King Buxton (now King B Powerworks) on Judges' Decision

Series 3 Defeated Overkill in a furious first heat battle then overpowered Centurion, assisted by an arena spike. Offered up to Matilda by King Buxton in the Heat Final, but escaped to return the compliment by ramming King B into Shunt who axed them. 101 won on points. Shunted Scutter's Revenge into House Robots to win first Semi, then fought an epic battle with Hypno-Disc, which they lost on a Judges' Decision.

Series 4 Immobilized Major Tom by shunting it into the Arena wall. In a disappointing Heat Final, the judges awarded the match to Dominator 2. Winners of Series 4 Tag-Team contest with King B3

Notes

'Tracks are fun with 101' is the team slogan. 101 isn't afraid of flippers but they have nightmares about Razer who can get underneath them if they're not careful. They'd love to go head-to-head with Suicidal Tendencies to prove that 101 is best on tracks.

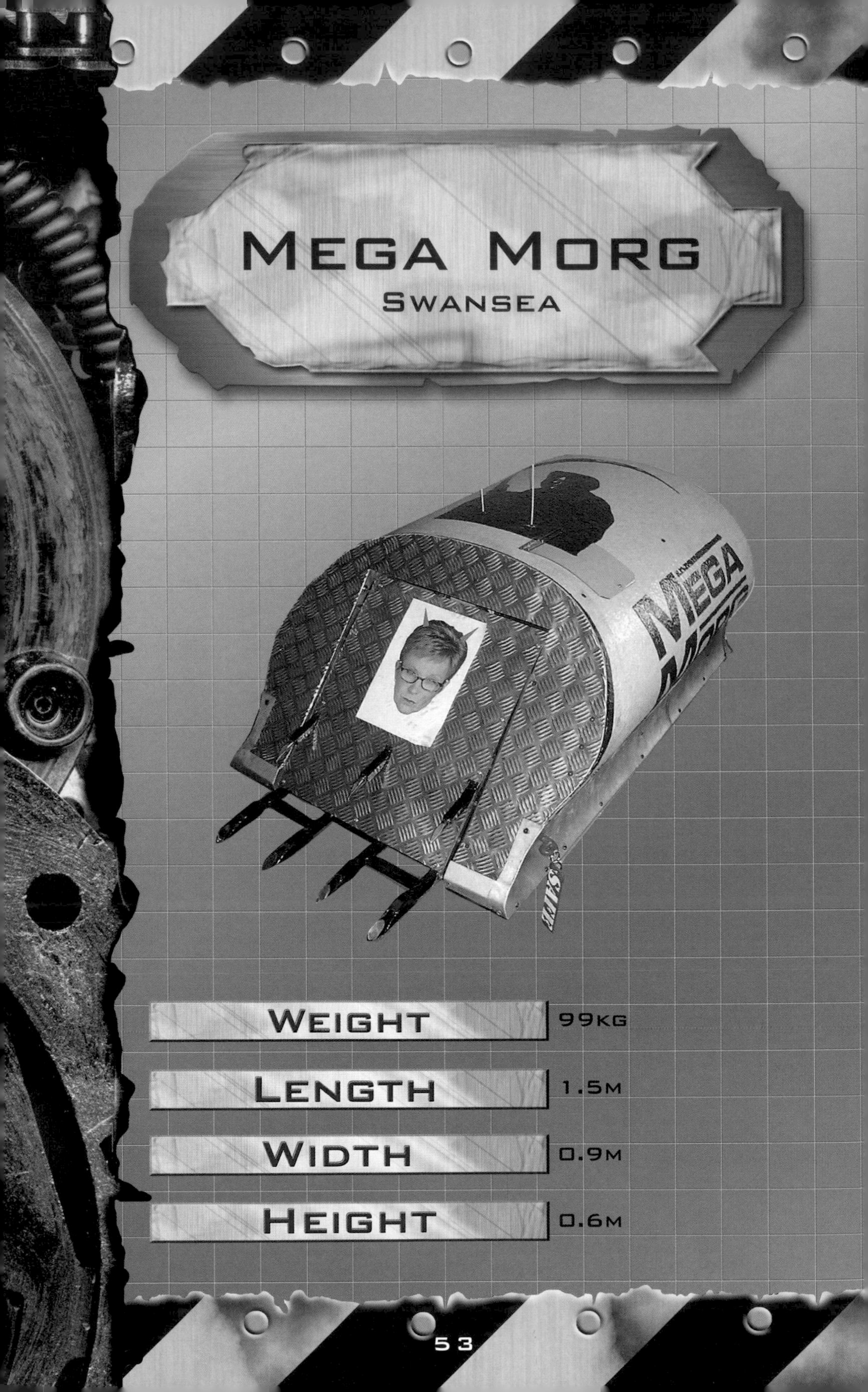

MEGA MORG

SWANSEA

WEIGHT	99KG
LENGTH	1.5M
WIDTH	0.9M
HEIGHT	0.6M

Speed

12 mph

Turning Circle

0

Clearance

1mm

Power

2 x 24v 750-watt Bosch motors

Weapons

Front-mounted shunting plate with pneumatic ramming and lifting spikes. Lifting operation now much faster than before. Self-righting roll-over shape

Armour

Silicon-impregnated Kevlar shell to blunt drills and saws. Titanium side skirts

Team

Dorian Caudy (Captain), Mark Hooper and Huw White

Team Battle History

Series 4 As The Morgue. Defeated in the first three-way melée bout with Scar and Firestorm II, The Morgue progressed in the heats anyway due to Scar being unfit for further combat. Beat Ming II, ramming and lifting until Ming 2 suffered mechanical failure. Rammed, rolled and ultimately immobilized in a second encounter with Firestorm II in the Heat Final, they lost despite Firestorm II driving themselves into the pit. Judges ruled that The Morgue were defeated before Firestorm II got careless

Notes

Upgraded batteries give Mega Morg more power to cope with the increased weight of its improved, faster-action spiking and lifting spears. Teamed with Irish stalwarts Diótóir, the pair form a formidable Celtic alliance

MAJOR TOM

ISLE OF SHEPPEY

WEIGHT	100KG
LENGTH	1.6M
WIDTH	0.96M
HEIGHT	0.85M

Speed
20 mph

Turning Circle
0

Clearance
50mm

Power
2 x 12v golf-caddy motors

Weapons
Electric flywheel blade mounted at front

Armour
Bodyshell mainly fibreglass

Team
Henry Ryan (Captain), John Morris and Joe Brown

Team Battle History
Series 4 Armed with a lifting ramp, Major Tom (Mark 1) was keen to have a go at 101 in the first heat, but 101's superior power and aggression were too much for them. Shunted, rammed and slammed into the arena wall, Major Tom was immobilized

Notes
The original Major Tom was made from a garden water barrel. The new version is a fairground bumper car that has been travelling the country since 1978! Teamed with Bigger Brother for optimum combination of flipping and cutting weapons

Bigger Brother

Brighton

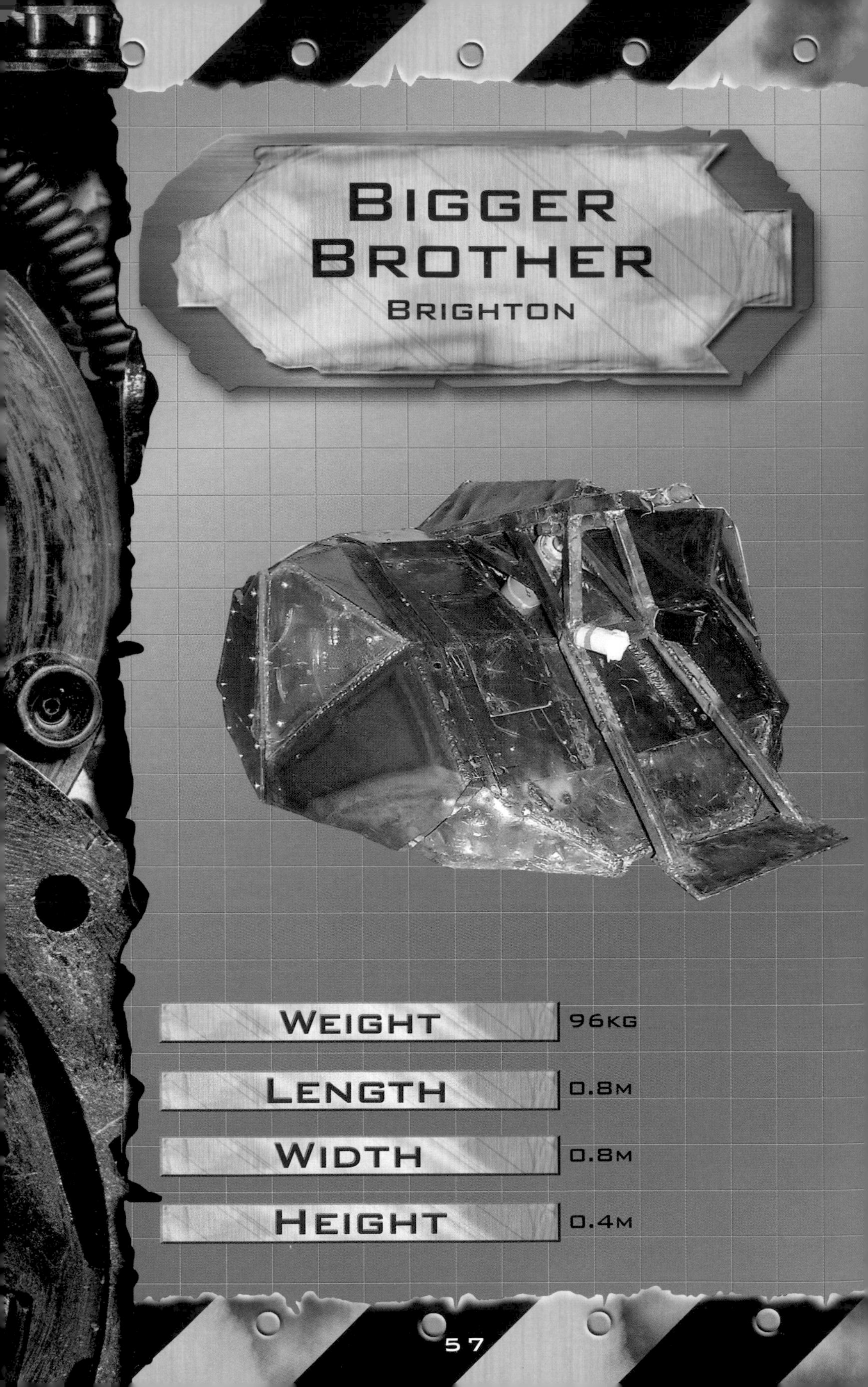

Weight	96kg
Length	0.8m
Width	0.8m
Height	0.4m

Speed
10 mph

Turning Circle
0

Clearance
0mm

Power
2 x truck windscreen-wiper motors running off 2 batteries

Weapons
Flipping blade powered by a JCB hydraulic ram. Can flip a Mini car with a high-speed (0.01 seconds) action

Armour
Steel shell with bulletproof polycarbonate

Team
Joe Watts (Captain), Ian Watts and Ellie Watts

Team Battle History
SERIES 3 As Big Brother. Made a big impact when they took on Grim Reaper in a ramming contest in the heats. Both suffered battle damage but Big Brother won on points. Flipped Sir Chromalot to win Heat Final. Mace II flipped them into Sgt Bash in the Semi-Final and it was all over

SERIES 4 Bigger Brother suffered a CO_2 leak from their flipper mechanism in the heats against Bulldog Breed II, losing power to their weapon. Bulldog Breed II flipped them to win

Notes
Updated gyroscopic controls now make Bigger Brother more manoeuvrable and easier to control. They're not afraid to take on anyone, but only want to fight the best. They don't see any point in fighting a robot that's no good. As they put it, 'No guts, no glory'.

Comengetorix

Isle of Wight

Comengetorix

Weight	93kg
Length	1.3m
Width	0.88m
Height	0.31m

Speed
15 mph

Turning Circle
0

Clearance
5mm

Power
2 x 750-watt gas turbine starter motors

Weapons
Pneumatic lifter and axe now with faster operation than before and more power. Lifter can raise up to 200kg

Armour
Mainly aluminium with titanium top panels

Team
Ian Gear (Captain), Alistair Curtis-Horsfall and Tom Curtis-Horsfall

Team Battle History
SERIES 2 As Vercingetorix. Progressed through heats until they came up against Haardvark at which point they suffered mechanical failure and were plunged into the pit by Sir Killalot

SERIES 3 As Vercingetorix. In a cautious sparring match with Terrorpin, the two tried to sacrifice each other to the House Robots. Finally, Terrorpin, shunted Vercingetorix into the pit. Terrorpin then drove themselves in too, but still won

SERIES 4 As Vercingetorix. Despite embedding their axe in Spawn, they were shunted around the arena and lost the heat to Spawn

Notes
Comengetorix would love to meet up with Spawn Again (formerly Spawn of Scutter and Scutter's Revenge) for a re-match, despite the fact that they are Tag-Team partners

SPAWN AGAIN
ESSEX

WEIGHT	79KG
LENGTH	1.25M
WIDTH	0.85M
HEIGHT	0.5M

Speed
25 mph

Turning Circle
0

Clearance
7mm

Power
2 x Ford Granada starter motors

Weapons
Pneumatic CO2-powered flipper with spike to lock on to enemy. Flipper will lift 350kg

Armour
3mm Polycarbonate

Team
Darren Ball (Captain), Graham Warner and Luke Jackman

Team Battle History
SERIES 3 As Scutter's Revenge. Armed with a bulldozing scoop, they shunted Zeus into the pit in the heats and followed them up with Thermidor. Then came the battle with Pussycat who were disqualified when their blade shattered, allowing Scutter through to the Semi-Finals. In the Semis, 101 shunted Scutter into the House Robots, who attacked, and Scutter was finished

SERIES 4 As Spawn of Scutter. Disposed of Vercingetorix (now Comengetorix) in heats before ramming Knightmare to a standstill and offering them up to Shunt. Scutter were lifted and wedged against the arena wall to lose to Panic Attack in the Semi-Final

Notes
Spawn of Scutter's flipper is now powerful enough to toss other robots into the air. Their weakness, though, may be their topside armour, which they want to make double-skinned to protect against spiking

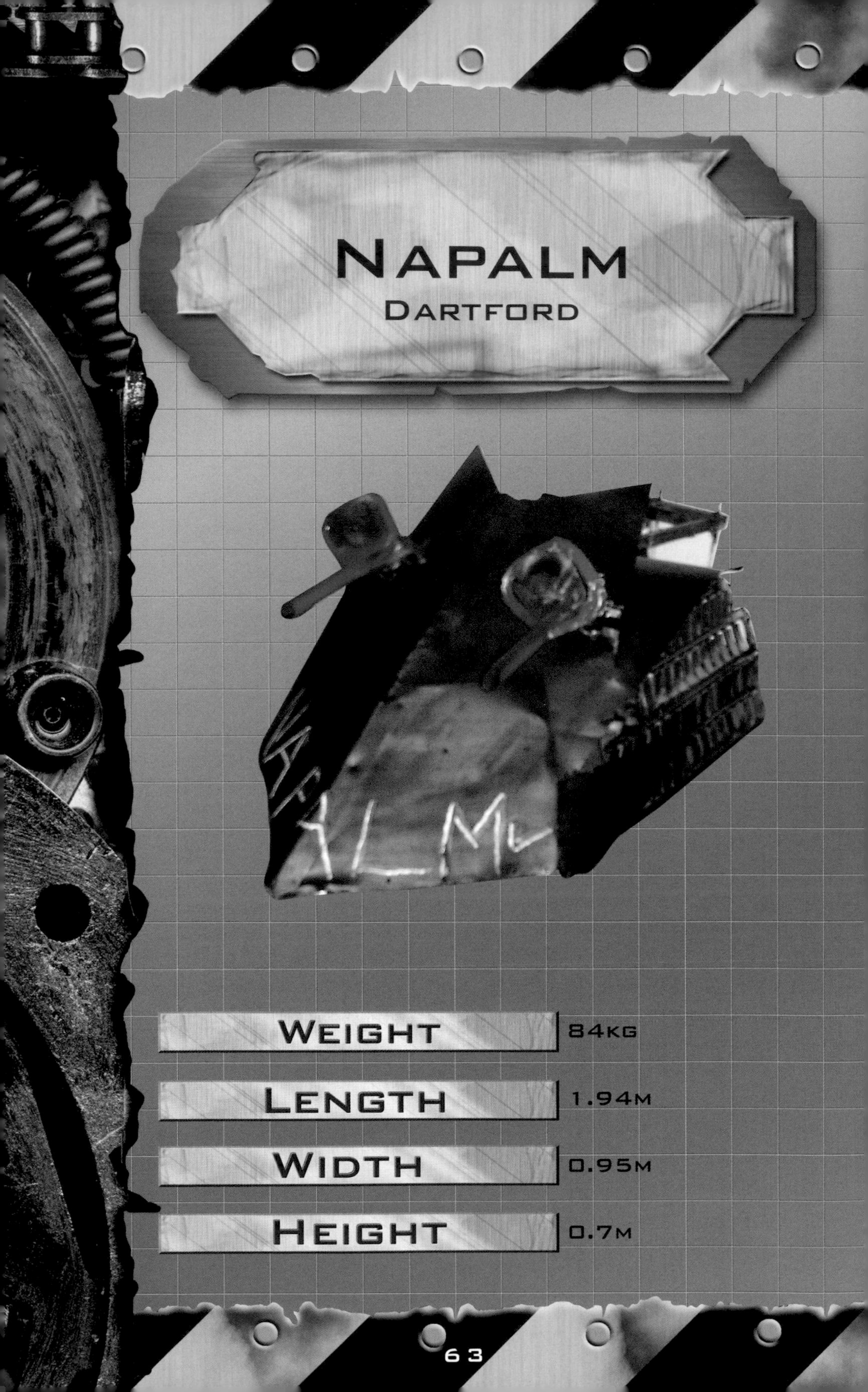

NAPALM
DARTFORD

WEIGHT	84KG
LENGTH	1.94M
WIDTH	0.95M
HEIGHT	0.7M

Speed

20 mph

Turning Circle

0

Clearance

20mm

Power

2 x 12v wheelchair motors

Weapons

Armour-piercing mandibles and reinforced steel front ram

Armour

Titanium hull with mild steel side panels

Team

David Crosby (Captain), Clare Greenaway and Vikki Allgood

Team Battle History

SERIES 1 As Detonator.
Detonator was a petrol-engined robot, but was eliminated in the trial heats when its batteries failed
SERIES 2 Armed with a chainsaw that Sir Killalot ripped off in the Gauntlet Trial, Napalm nevertheless managed to immobilize Killalot. Defeated Demolition Demon to go into Semi-Finals, where Killalot got his own back by picking Napalm up and toasting them over the flame pit during the Pinball Tournament
SERIES 3 Defeated Kater Killer in first heat, then turned Robopig over with the help of Shunt in the next heat. Also had the satisfaction of seeing Killalot stray too close to the flame pit and catch light! Napalm was then rammed to pieces by Steg-O-Saw-Us in the Heat Final
SERIES 4 As Shadow of Napalm. The new Napalm design for Series 4 couldn't stand up to the devastating axe of Dominator 2, who trashed Napalm in the heats before shunting them into the pit

Notes

With Shadow of Napalm a pile of junk, it was back to the old Napalm for Robot Wars Extreme. A ground-up rebuild was required to prepare for the competition and the combination of Napalm's weapons with Sir Chromalot's flipper and spikes should make them strong Tag-Team contenders

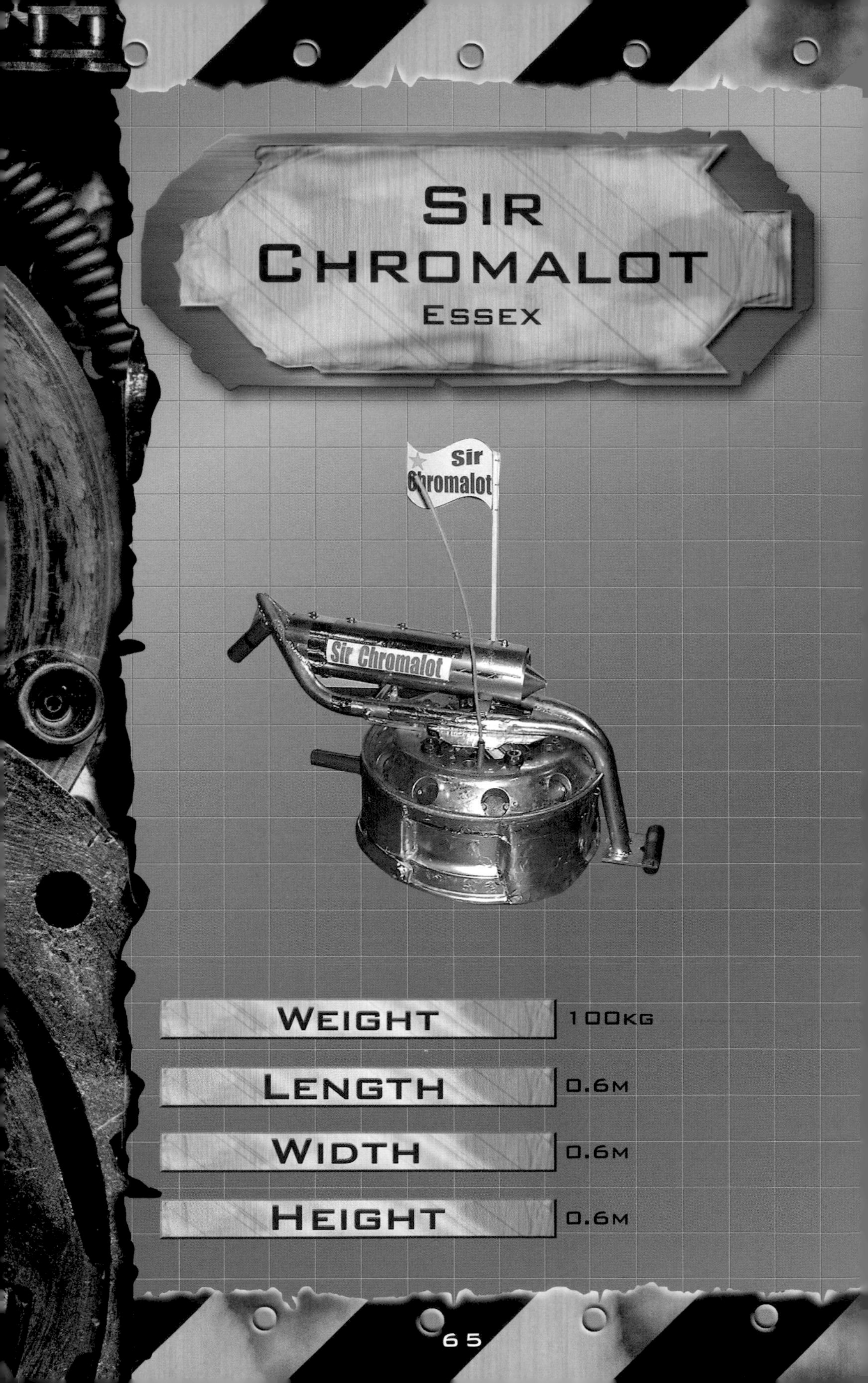

Sir Chromalot

Essex

Weight	100kg
Length	0.6m
Width	0.6m
Height	0.6m

Speed
15 mph

Turning Circle
0

Clearance
3mm

Power
2 x 750-watt Bosch motors

Weapons
Pneumatic flipper and ramming spike. Reverse arm of flipper has spike bearing down with 15 tonnes of pressure at the tip

Armour
Steel truck wheel hub

Team
Steve Merrill (Captain) and Ray Tait

Team Battle History
Series 3
Disabled Shell Shock's weapon in first heat and seemed set to win until suffering mechanical failure and being shunted into the pit by Sir Killalot. Controversial Judges' Decision awarded the bout to Chromalot anyway. They had less luck in the next heat when they were trounced by Big Brother
Series 4 Driven on to an arena spike by Steel Avenger in their heat, Chromalot ultimately ended up being shunted into the pit

Notes
Sir Chromalot's team most want to get to grips with the Plunderbirds (or Plundergirls as they call them) as a behind-the-scenes rivalry has developed that can only really be settled by all-out combat in the arena

Steel Avenger

Colchester

Weight	100kg
Length	1.3m
Width	0.7m
Height	0.8m

Speed

20 mph

Turning Circle

0

Clearance

20 mm

Power

2 x 750-watt Bosch motors

Weapons

Now armed with a pneumatic lifter at the rear to supplement its pneumatic axe and front shunting blade

Armour

Aluminium and polycarbonate

Team

John Willoughby (Captain), Jacky Willoughby and Tony Bates

Team Battle History

SERIES 3 Defeated Schumey Too with a little help from the arena spike, which sent Schumey on their way into the pit. In the next heat they faced Diótóir and poked one of its eyes out before being flipped. Diótóir ended up in flames (as usual) but won anyway

SERIES 4 Their axe blows missed Sir Chromalot most of the time but they eventually won the heat by shoving it into the pit. Rammed and tipped over by Wild Thing in the following heat, their self-righting mechanism failed and it was all over. Winner of Best Engineered Robot Award in Series 4

Notes

Two side arms linked to Steel Avenger's lifter are supposed to right them if they are flipped, but battle damage can take its toll as they found to their cost in Series 4. Having previously felt vulnerable from the rear, the new flipper means that they can attack in either direction

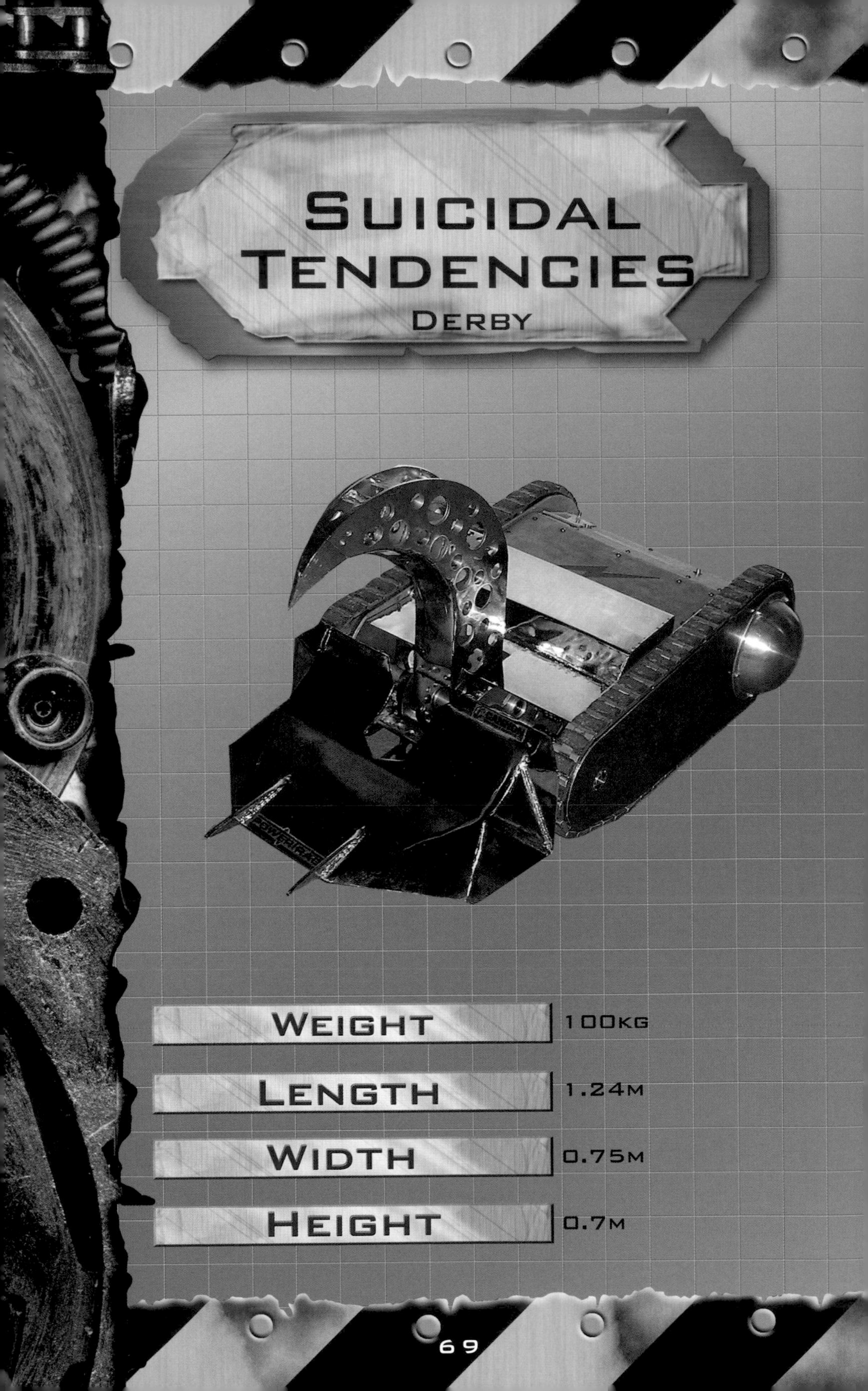

Suicidal Tendencies

Derby

Weight	100kg
Length	1.24m
Width	0.75m
Height	0.7m

Speed
10 mph

Turning Circle
0

Clearance
15mm

Power
2 x 750-watt Bosch motors

Weapons
New electric claw, steel spikes and front scoop

Armour
2.3mm titanium shell

Team
Andrew Jeffrey (Captain), Martin Jeffrey and Charles Binns

Team Battle History
SERIES 3
Scorched
Forklift over the flame pit in the first heat before shunting them to Sir Killalot, who picked them up and posted them in the pit. Then enjoyed a narrow victory against Razer Blade (who drove into the pit and were helped out by Killalot!) despite a damaged track. Lost to Mace II in heat Final when they were shunted into the House Robots, who did their usual maximum damage
SERIES 4 As Suicidal Tendencies 2. Punctured Wheelosaurus's petrol tank and then shoved it into the flames. With a damaged track in the heat Final against Wheely Big Cheese, the Cheese tried to shunt them into the pit, but missed and drove themselves in instead. Controversial Judges' Decision awarded the bout to the Cheese as Suicidal Tendencies was deemed immobilized

Notes
Completely redesigned for Robot Wars Extreme, only the gearboxes for each track have been retained from the previous version. Able to run either way up, the hubs help to prevent Suicidal Tendencies being stranded on its side

CERBERUS

HAMMERSMITH

WEIGHT	99KG
LENGTH	1.46M
WIDTH	0.92M
HEIGHT	0.58M

Speed
16 mph

Turning Circle
0

Clearance
20mm

Power
2 x 750-watt Bosch motors

Weapons
Steel jaw pincers and steel ramming claws

Armour
Titanium bodyshell

Team
Theo Kaccoufa (Captain), Vassili Vassileou and Alex Wink

Team Battle History
SERIES 3 Won their first heat when Killerhurtz drove themselves into the pit. Took advantage of Griffon's drive malfunction to help them into the pits in the next heat. Cerberus was then flame-grilled over the fire pit by Thing II before being tipped over in a hard-fought Heat Final

SERIES 4 Knocked out in the three-way opening heat when they were rammed and then flipped by V-Max

Notes
The Cerberus team don't like many other robots. In fact, they claim to hate all other robots, especially flippers. To combat being flipped again, Cerberus has a new self-righting mechanism

Thermidor II

Norwich

Weight	95kg
Length	1m
Width	0.8m
Height	0.34m

Speed
15 mph

Turning Circle
0

Clearance
5–25mm

Power
2 x 750-watt Bosch motors

Weapons
New wedge-shaped shunting and grasping claws. Upgraded flipper

Armour
Aluminium body panels

Team
David Harding (Captain) and Ian Harvey

Team Battle History
SERIES 3 As Thermidor. An easy first-round heat-win against Plunderstorm (now Plunderbird 5), where the House Robots did most of the work, led to a scrappy encounter with Scutter's Revenge, who eventually pushed Thermidor into the pit

SERIES 4 Flipped Dreadnought XP-1 to win their first heat, before meeting Kronic the Wedgehog and snapping off their flipper in the Heat Final. Put on a good show against Pussycat in their Semi-Final bout, flipping them in the air before Pussycat sliced open Thermidor's top armour. Pussycat won on points

Notes
Refinements to Thermidor II include an upgraded steel flipper. The flipper bending almost caused them to lose their Series 4 match with Kronic. There are now also two flipper gas tanks to make sure that they can go on flipping for a whole bout. Claws have a new wedge-shape for shunting

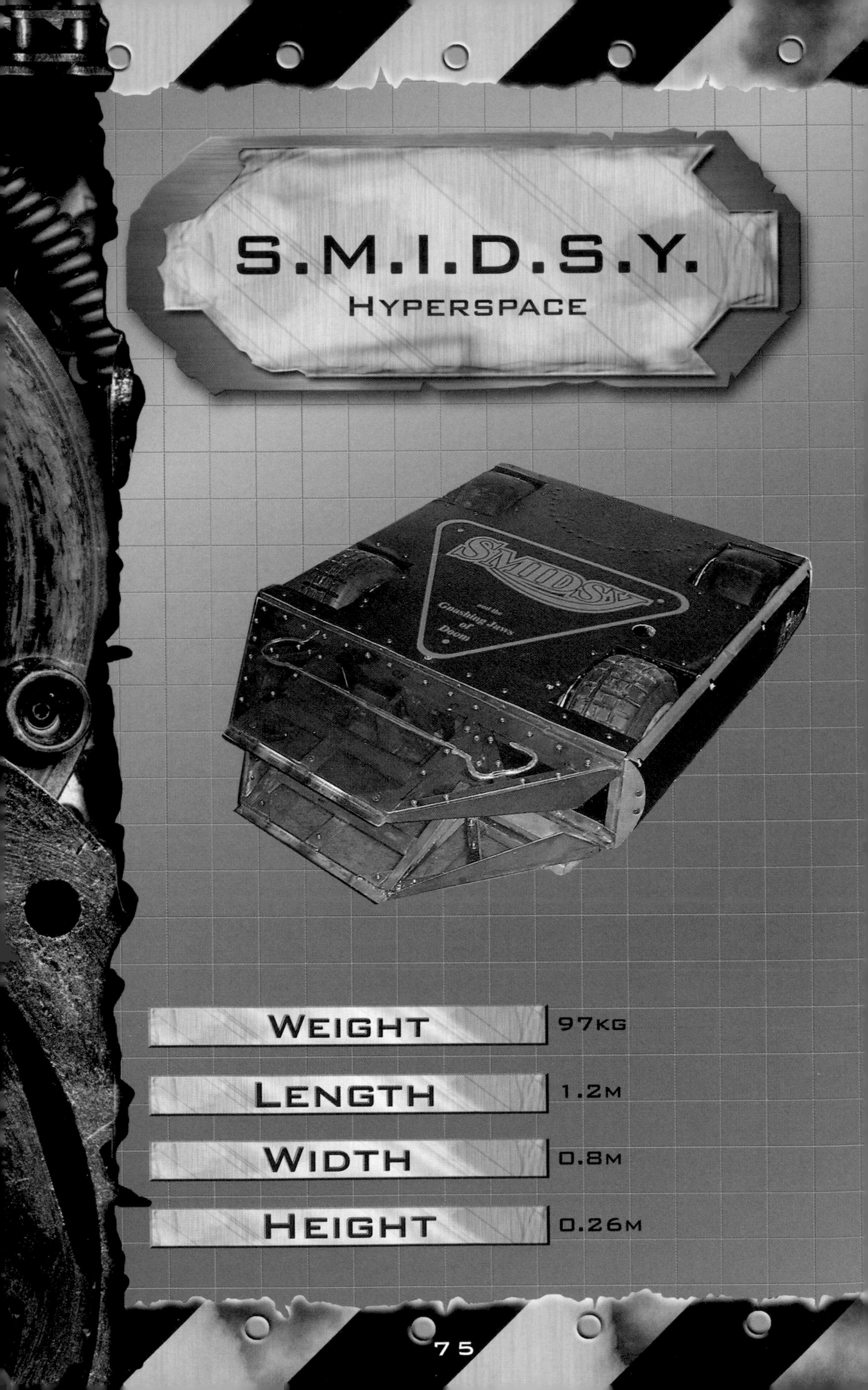

S.M.I.D.S.Y.

Hyperspace

Weight	97kg
Length	1.2m
Width	0.8m
Height	0.26m

Speed

10 mph

Turning Circle

0

Clearance

25mm (adjustable)

Power

2 x 750-watt Bosch motors

Weapons

Ramming, flipping and piercing 'Gnashing Jaws of Doom'. Also a rear-mounted 4-tooth cutting disc spinning at 5600 rpm

Armour

Titanium top and bottom. Polypropylene-backed with titanium elsewhere

Team

Mik Reed (captain), Robin Bennett and Andy Pugh

Team Battle History

SERIES 3 Lost their first round heat against the manic Rattus Rattus, who battered S.M.I.D.S.Y. before accidentally sacrificing themselves to Dead Metal. Flying in the air and smoking after an excursion over the flame pit, Rattus still had the energy to push S.M.I.D.S.Y. into the pit

SERIES 4 Won their heat by repeatedly smashing Aggrobot 2 into the arena wall until it was immobilized. Succumbed to Panic Attack in the heat Final. Panic Attack lifted S.M.I.D.S.Y. over the flame pit before dropping them in the pit

Notes

S.M.I.D.S.Y. have developed a specialized offensive spin-manoeuvre to baffle the enemy – especially useful now that they can attack in either direction. The new rear-cutting disc spins at a speed equivalent to 200 mph

Sumpthing
Leicester

Weight	90kg
Length	1.4m
Width	1m
Height	0.4m

Speed

20 mph

Turning Circle

0

Clearance

8mm

Power

4 x 800-watt car starter motors

Weapons

Interchangeable bulldozing shunt, twin circular saws, ramming spikes and pick axe

Armour

Steel bodyshell

Team

Richard Dig (Captain), Geoff Germainey and Paul Bacon

Team Battle History

SERIES 3
Suffered badly in first round heat when Pit Bull shunted them over the fire pit and they conked out. Sgt Bash then sliced and diced them before Sir Killalot dumped them in the pit

SERIES 4 Sumpthing took a battering from Mousetrap in their heat, but seemed to be gaining the upper hand, charged in for the kill, missed, and knocked themselves out on the arena wall. Immobilized, they lost

Notes

Sumpthing's team regards it as a low-tech robot, and admit that 'every time we turn it on something remarkable happens'. They have never actually been beaten, but have always somehow contrived to beat themselves. When it all goes right, though, watch out!

BATTLE DAMAGE

Battle damage will always be sustained in the metal-crunching mayhem of a full-on arena confrontation, and most robots are designed not only to be as resistant to damage as possible, but also to be infinitely repairable.

For the unlucky few, the damage may be terminal and the team will take the bits of their fallen gladiator home in a couple of carrier bags. For most competitors, though, it's a case of rolling up their sleeves and undertaking whatever repairs are necessary to make their robot fully combat-ready again as quickly as possible.

Wounded warriors are retrieved from the arena and wheeled back to the pits where each team is allocated a workbench to prepare and repair their robots. Every team brings with them essential tools and spare parts with which to work on their robots but, away from their own home workshops, they may not have all of the tools and parts that they need.

The Robot Wars technical-support team is always on hand to provide whatever assistance they can to keep the robots running. There's no show without

THE STARS, AFTER ALL, AND THE PRIORITY IS TO GET DAMAGED ROBOTS THAT ARE STILL IN CONTENTION UP AND RUNNING AGAIN IN TIME FOR THEIR NEXT SCHEDULED BOUT. THE PITS ARE ALWAYS AN AREA OF INTENSE ACTIVITY. ON ONE BENCH YOU MAY SEE CUTTERS, GRINDERS OR WELDERS IN ACTION WHILE ON ANOTHER BENCH DELICATE ELECTRONIC CIRCUITRY IS BEING PAINSTAKINGLY REBUILT.

SPECIAL WEAPONS SYSTEMS AND DEVIOUS DEVICES HAVE ALWAYS BEEN CLOSELY GUARDED SECRETS BUT MOST ROBOTEERS HAVE, IN THE PAST, BEEN WILLING TO LEND ONE ANOTHER A HAND. AS COMPETITION GROWS EVER FIERCER, HOWEVER, UNSAVOURY FEUDS AND VENDETTAS HAVE STARTED TO SPILL OVER FROM THE ARENA INTO THE PITS. DESPITE THE FACT THAT TAMPERING WITH ANOTHER TEAM'S ROBOT IS THE MOST HEINOUS CRIME A ROBOTEER CAN COMMIT, YOU HAVE TO BE CAREFUL WHOSE HELP YOU ACCEPT. IS HE A GOOD SAMARITAN OR A SPYING SABOTEUR ...?

MAYHEM

THE MOST MANIC, ACTION-PACKED OF ALL THE ROBOT WARS SCENARIOS, THE MELÉE, IS BROUGHT INTO PLAY IN MAYHEM. A MELÉE CONSISTS OF THREE OR MORE ROBOTS MANGLING METAL TOGETHER IN THE ARENA.

RULES

TWELVE BATTLES, EACH FEATURING THREE COMBATANTS, WILL BE FOUGHT. NORMAL ROBOT WARS RULES APPLY, WITH THE LAST ROBOT STILL FUNCTIONING, OR THE ROBOT THE JUDGES DECIDE HAS SCORED MOST POINTS BEING DECLARED THE WINNER. THE TWELVE WINNERS WILL THEN PROGRESS TO THE ANNIHILATOR CONTESTS. THERE WILL BE TWO ANNIHILATOR CONTESTS, EACH STARTING WITH SIX ROBOTS IN THE ARENA TOGETHER. THE SIX ROBOTS WILL FIGHT UNTIL ONE IS IMMOBILIZED. THE FIVE SURVIVORS WILL THEN BATTLE ON UNTIL ANOTHER ONE IS IMMOBILIZED, AND SO ON UNTIL ONLY ONE VICTORIOUS ROBOT REMAINS.

THE MAYHEM COMPETITION, THEREFORE, PRODUCES ONE WINNER FROM EACH OF THE TWO ANNIHILATORS. THESE TWO ANNIHILATOR CHAMPIONS ARE BOUND TO BE CARRYING SOME HEFTY BATTLE SCARS AFTER SUCH SPECTACULAR BOUTS, BUT AS SOON AS THEY'VE LICKED THEIR WOUNDS THEY MAY WANT TO SQUARE UP TO EACH OTHER TO SEE WHO'S THE TOUGHEST OF THE LOT!

Battle Board

Mayhem Combatants

Competing groups are top secret until just prior to competition!

Bigger Brother
S.M.I.D.S.Y.
Gemini
Hypno-Disc
Wild Thing
Behemoth
Splinter
Wheely Big Cheese
Napalm
Comengetorix
Aggrobot 3
3 Stegs to Heaven
Spawn Again
Ming 3
Atomic
King B Powerworks
Killertron 1
Steel Avenger

101
Bulldog Breed III
Pussycat
X-Terminator
Diótóir
Mega Morg
Thermidor II
Firestorm III
Stinger
Fighting Torque
Sumpthing
Judge Shred 2½
Tornado
Suicidal Tendencies
Mousetrap
Plunderbird 5
Panic Attack
Spirit of Knightmare

MING 3

KETTERING

WEIGHT	100KG
LENGTH	1.5M
WIDTH	0.72M
HEIGHT	0.8M

Speed

15 mph

Turning Circle

0

Clearance

13mm

Power

2 x 500-watt electric motors

Weapons

Razer-style crushing spike. Lifting scoop that can easily pick up 100kg. Rear spike for protection from behind

Armour

Stainless steel, titanium, aluminium

Team

Andrew Cotterell (captain), Alexander Cotterell, Oliver Cotterell

Team Battle History

SERIES 3 As Ming. Battered by Mortis's hammer, then tipped over, Ming's spinning blade weapon was destroyed and Mortis was triumphant

SERIES 4 As Ming 2. Defeated by The Morgue (now Mega Morg) in their heat. Ming managed to flip Morgue, but was spiked, lifted and eventually immobilized

Notes

Now more heavily armed than ever before, Ming's spikes and lifter are a deadly combination. They do confess to having a weak spot, but are obviously keeping it to themselves – no need to give Mortis or Mega Morg another chance to defeat them!

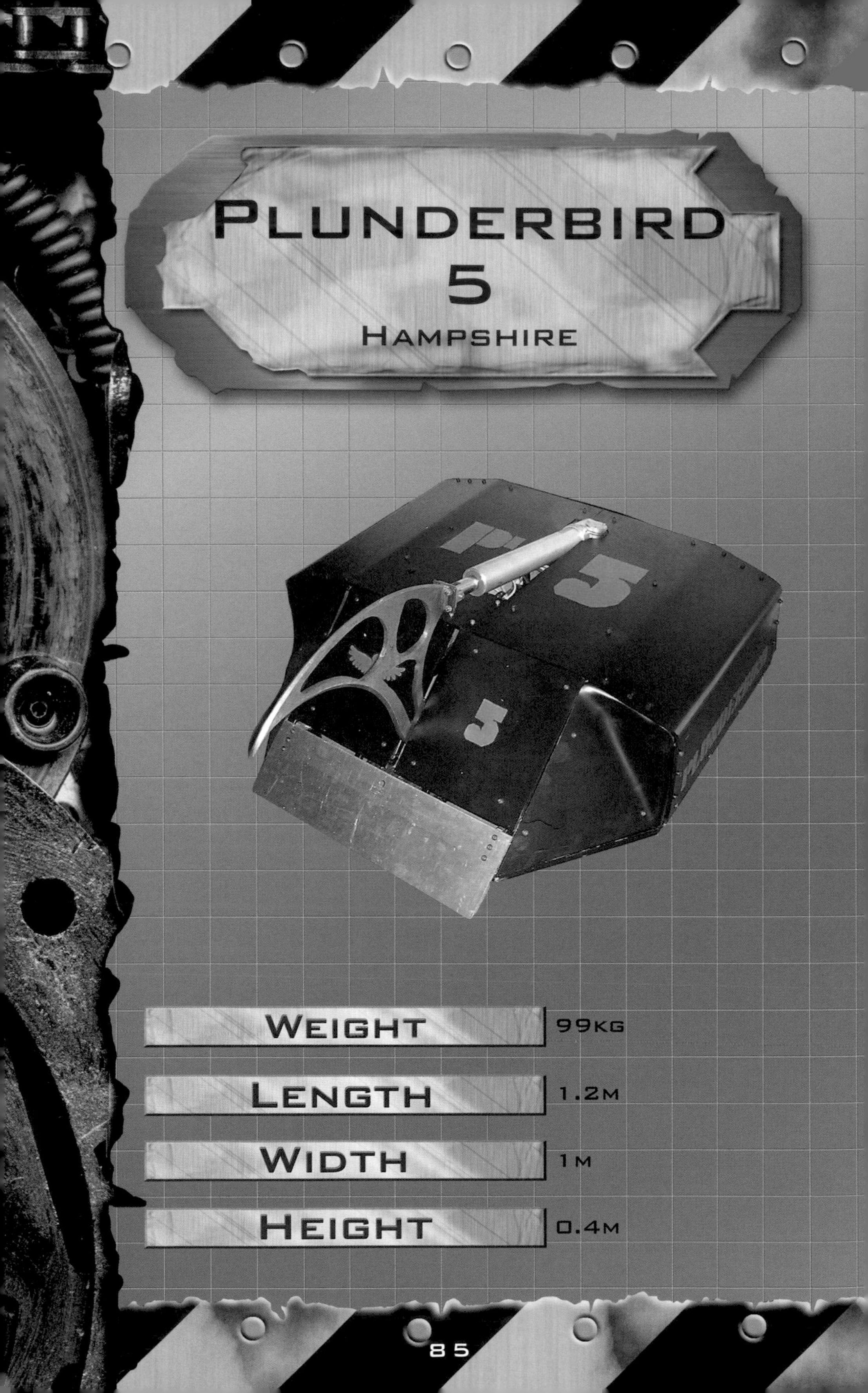

PLUNDERBIRD 5

HAMPSHIRE

WEIGHT	99KG
LENGTH	1.2M
WIDTH	1M
HEIGHT	0.4M

Speed

20 mph

Turning Circle

0

Clearance

5mm

Power

2 x 750-watt Bosch electric motors

Weapons

Plunderthocker piercing claw run on 750-watt linear actuator

Armour

6mm polycarbonate

Team

Mike Onslow (Captain) and Bryan Kilburn

Team Battle History

SERIES 1 As Plunderbird 1.
Winner of Best Designed Robot Award in Series 1. Nevertheless, its optional circular saw or piercing spike couldn't help it when it got itself stuck on a grille and was forced to retire

SERIES 2 As Plunderbird 2. Defeated Enzyme and The Mule to go through to the Semi-Final trials, but was eliminated when Matilda lopped off their aerial

SERIES 3 As Plunderstorm. Appeared to stall and was attacked by Thermidor in their heat before the House Robots closed in and finished them off

SERIES 4 As Plunderbird 4. Malfunctioning drive put them at a disadvantage to Knightmare (now Spirit of Knightmare) in their heat when they became locked in combat. Plunderbird 4 was eventually flipped by Knightmare and lost

Notes

The Plunderbird team like to make their feelings known and have told the Sir Chromalot team that they think they are a bunch of girlies. The two teams want a chance to settle their differences in the arena

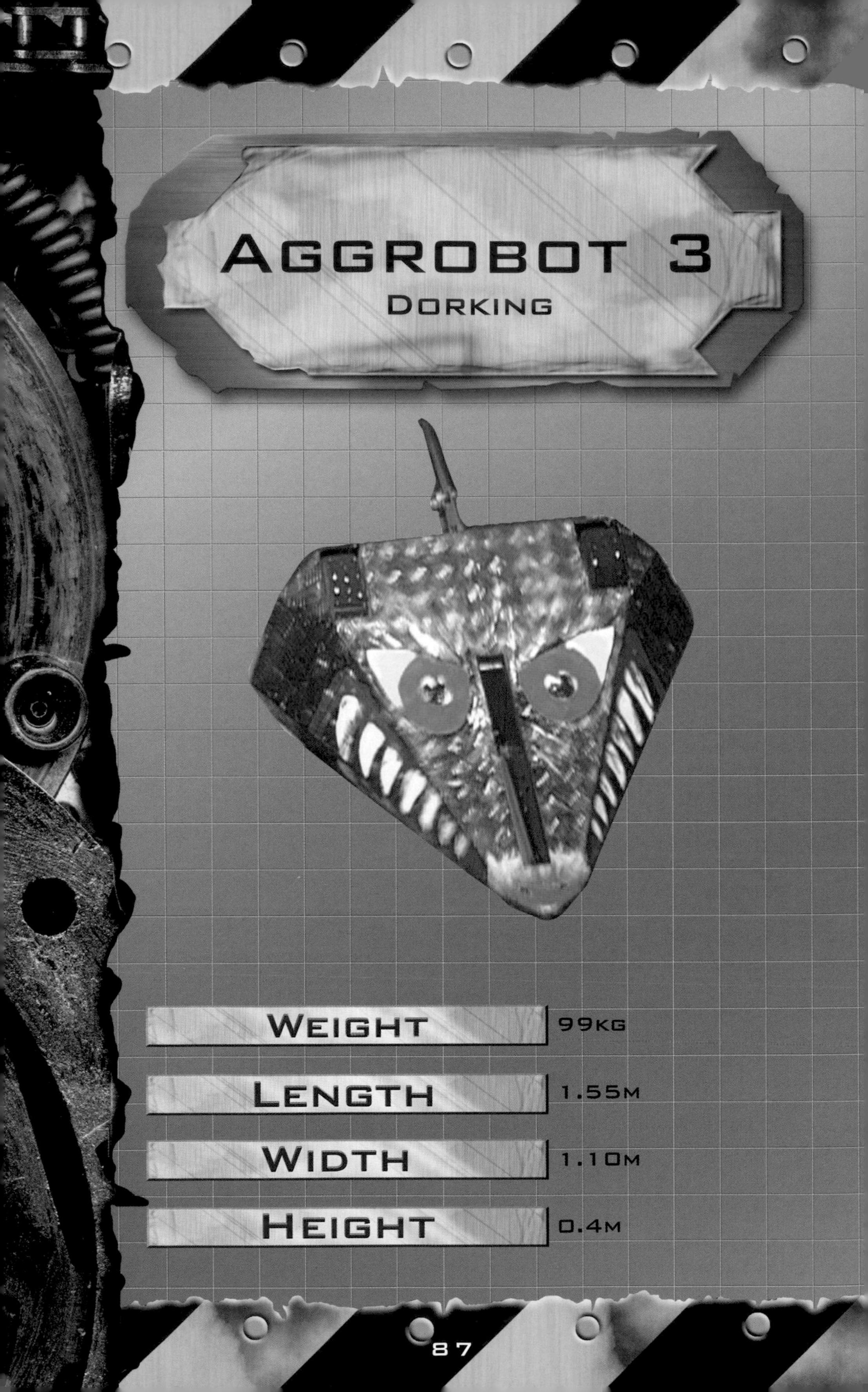

AGGROBOT 3

DORKING

WEIGHT	99KG
LENGTH	1.55M
WIDTH	1.10M
HEIGHT	0.4M

Speed

10 mph

Turning Circle

0

Clearance

25mm

Power

2 x wheelchair motors

Weapons

Hydraulic cutting jaws at rear and flipper arm at front

Armour

Aluminium alloy

Team

Peter Leach (Captain), Bob Leach, Jon Leach

Team Battle History

SERIES 3 As Aggrobot.
Aggrobot's spike, or 'hydraulic zonker', proved ineffective against Binky's shell in their heat, but the arena spike wasn't. Binky was immobilized while Aggrobot gamely dislodged Matilda's shell. Aggrobot then suffered severe damage at the hands (or claw) of Razer in their next heat before Razer conked out. Progressing to the Heat Final, Aggrobot then suffered a malfunction and was shunted on to the flame pit by Blade

SERIES 4 As Aggrobot 2. Shunted around the arena in their heat by S.M.I.D.S.Y. and then rammed into the arena wall until immobilized

Notes

Two-wheel-drive Aggrobot has independent power to each of the drive wheels to help keep it going in battle. Described by the team as 'stealth-shaped', one might have thought that stealth was the last thing you'd need in the Robot Wars arena. New weaponry for Robot Wars Extreme might give Aggrobot a bit more aggro

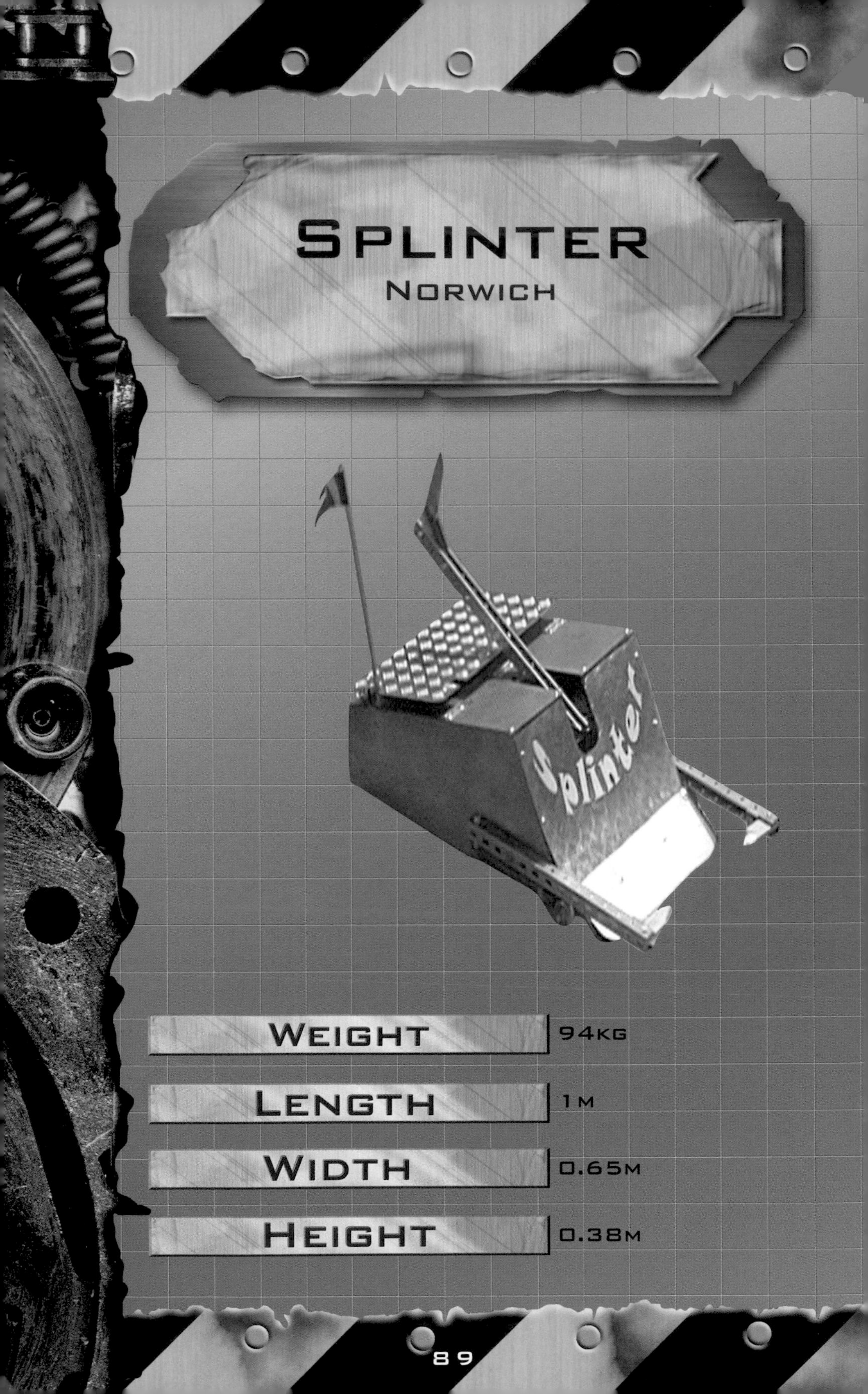

SPLINTER
NORWICH
Splinter
WEIGHT 94KG
LENGTH 1M
WIDTH 0.65M
HEIGHT 0.38M

Speed

15 mph

Turning Circle

0

Clearance

20 mm

Power

2 x 750-watt Bosch motors

Weapons

Pneumatic grabbing arms and pneumatic axe

Armour

Steel plate

Team

Craig Weightman (Captain) and Stuart Weightman

Team Battle History

SERIES 2 As Ivanhoe. Ivanhoe was an unusual helmet-shaped beast armed with a lance and an axe, and made good progress through the heats, but was eventually flipped and eliminated by GBH

SERIES 4 Managed to get a good grip of Killerhurtz in its jaws in their heat and waltzed them all over the arena shunting them against the walls. Killerhurtz eventually caught fire. Won the Heat Final against Eric on a Judges' decision and then it all went wrong in the Semis. Hypno-Disc was on top form and tore off Splinter's scoop before ripping into their armour and tearing them to shreds

Notes

Splinter's grabbing and piercing arms have always given them a useful advantage when it comes to using their scoop to shunt opponents into trouble, but the addition of a new axe means that while they're shunting they'll also be slicing and dicing. New, heavier armour (well, the old stuff wasn't up to much after Hypno-Disc was finished with them) and more power put the Splinter back in contention for Mayhem

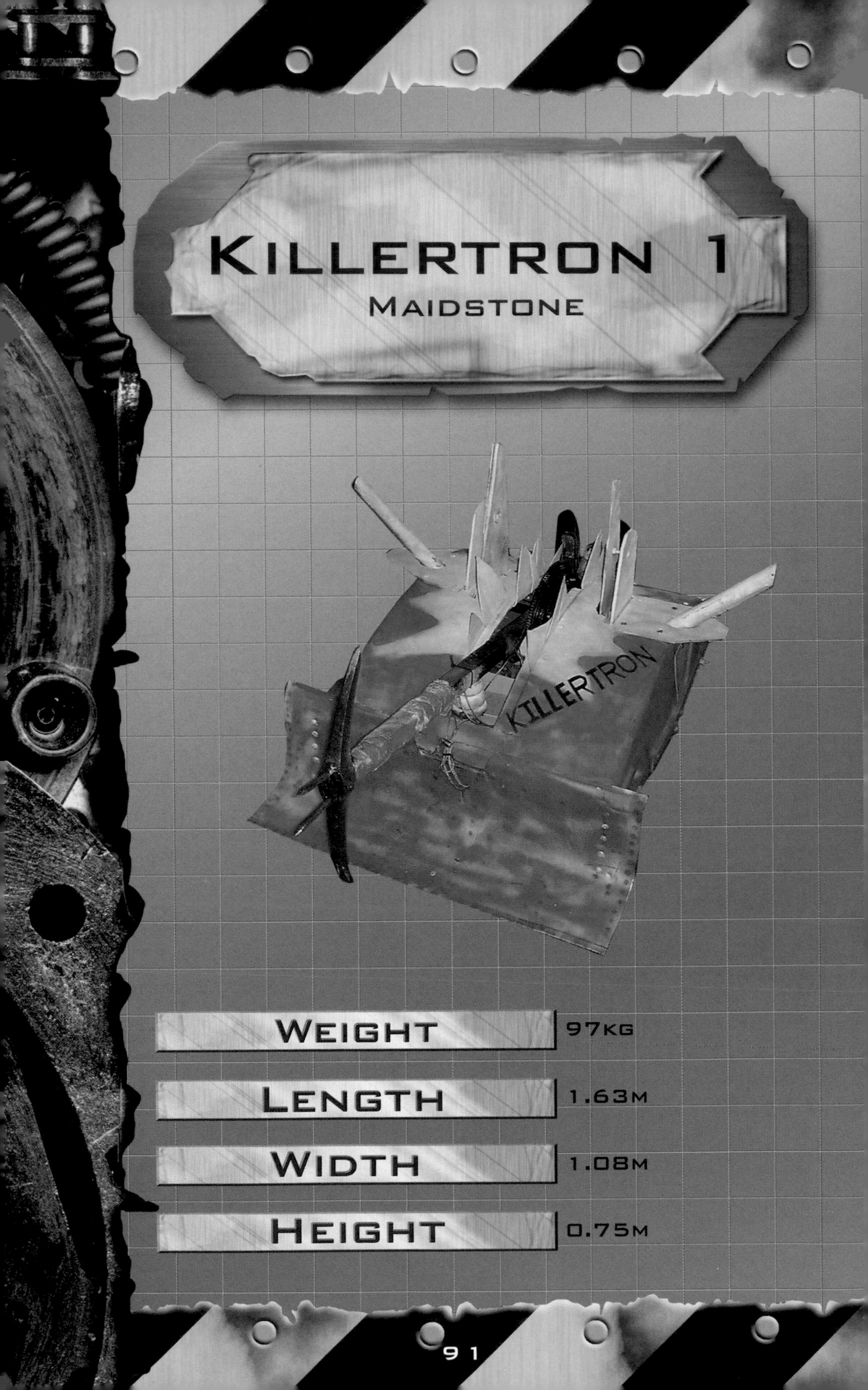
KILLERTRON 1
MAIDSTONE
KILLERTRON
WEIGHT
97KG
LENGTH
1.63M
WIDTH
1.08M
HEIGHT
0.75M

Speed

15 mph

Turning Circle

0

Clearance

2mm

Power

2 x 24v wheelchair motors

Weapons

Vicious axe

Armour

Steel chassis, plastic shell

Team

Richard Broad (Captain), Abdul Degia and Christopher Broad

Team Battle History

SERIES 1 As Killertron. Took what looked like a convincing victory in the Heat Semi against Shogun, but was overpowered by the mighty Roadblock in the Heat Final

SERIES 2 As Killertron. Battled their way through to the Semi-Finals, where they got the better of Behemoth before having to face Panic Attack in the Final. Panic Attack proved too much for Killertron and they were defeated

SERIES 4 As Killertron. Suffered a disastrous bout against Wheely Big Cheese. The Big Cheese flipped them several times and they just couldn't seem to stay upright, despite Matilda even helping to right them on one occasion

Notes

'The Robot with the Axe' is how Killertron has been billed in the past, but that axe has always tended to include a couple of tasty ramming spikes at the top of the shaft, and Killertron also deploys a shunting shovel. Fast for a heavyweight, Killertron has the potential to create utter havoc in Mayhem

MOUSETRAP

OXFORD AND BRISTOL

WEIGHT	95KG
LENGTH	1.5M
WIDTH	0.7M
HEIGHT	0.45M

Speed

8 mph

Turning Circle

0

Clearance

10mm

Power

2 x 24v motors, provided by Hawker

Weapons

Wedge-shaped body for shunting/tipping, plus flipping arm

Armour

Steel and Lexan

Team

Stan Launchbury (Captain) and Jason Launchbury

Team Battle History

SERIES 3 As Triterobot.
Spiking, shunting and clouds of smoke dominated Triterobot's heat with Evil Weevil. The Weevil eventually managed to tip Triterobot over on to its side to win
SERIES 4 Whacked Sumpthing several times with its bar, then appeared to lose power. Managed to dodge Sumpthing's death charge causing Sumpthing to slam themselves into the arena wall and knock themselves out. Mousetrap shunted and battered Little Fly in their Heat Final to progress to the Semis. Put up a brave fight against Stinger in the Semi-Final but repeated savage blows from Stinger's axe damaged Mousetrap's weapon, and Stinger won

Notes

Designed to look like an old-fashioned mousetrap and shaped like a wedge of cheese, this Mousetrap is after bigger prey than just a furry little rodent. The flipping bar can be used to lift or batter, and the sleek shape is intended to enable Mousetrap to drive right underneath its prey. Now almost 20kg heavier, Mousetrap boasts extra protection and more-powerful weapon action

ATOMIC
WORCESTER

WEIGHT	97KG
LENGTH	0.9M
WIDTH	0.76M
HEIGHT	0.28M

Speed
16 mph

Turning Circle
0

Clearance
Variable

Power
2 x 24v motors

Weapons
Lethal 60cm spike and flipper operating at up to 1000 psi pressure

Armour
Aluminium shell

Team
Stephen Bebb (Captain), Paul Francis and David Bebb

Team Battle History
Series 4

Shunted and lifted the far more experienced King B3 in their heat and showed impressive aggression by continuing to attack even after their flipper had been trashed. A well-deserved victory led to a meeting with Chaos II in the Heat Final. Chaos II flipped them like a rag doll ten times with the intention of flinging them clear out of the arena, although they didn't quite make it. Atomic were then severely assaulted by Sir Killalot and their tournament ended there

Notes
The incredible strength of Atomic's flipper and its wedge-shaped nose for shunting and riding under opponents make the yellow machine a dangerous adversary, not to be under-estimated despite what some might see as a lack of battle experience. Then there's that amazing ramming spike, which has yet to be used to its full potential. Definitely one to watch in Mayhem

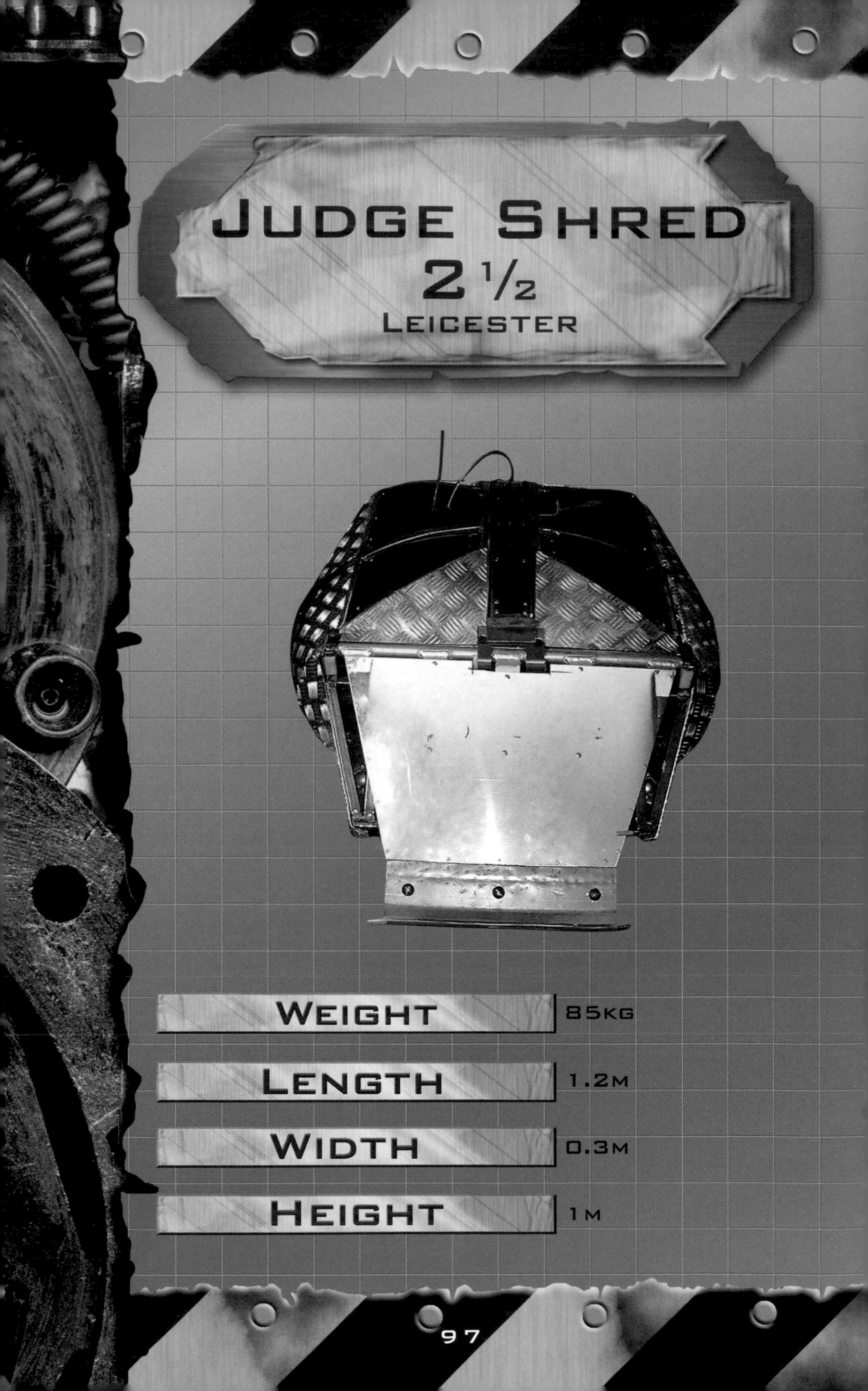
JUDGE SHRED
2 ½
LEICESTER
WEIGHT
85KG
LENGTH
1.2M
WIDTH
0.3M
HEIGHT
1M

Speed
12 mph

Turning Circle
0

Clearance
5–10mm

Power
2 x 750-watt industrial motors

Weapons
Rear-mounted pneumatic axe plus front-mounted flipper arm/axe

Armour
Polcarbonate and alloy shell

Team
Alan Blakeman (Captain), Paul Blakeman and Dave Cluley

Team Battle History
SERIES 3 As Judge Shred.
Shunted, lifted and chopped at Mr Punch to win their heat. Were then savaged by X-Terminator in the following heat. Axed, lifted and flung into the pit, X-Terminator soundly thrashed them
SERIES 4 As Judge Shred 2. Attempted to sacrifice Behemoth to the House Robots, but Behemoth retaliated by flipping Judge Shred. Disappointing failure of its self-righting arm meant that it stayed flipped

Notes
Judge Shred 2½'s axe strikes with tremendous speed and travels through a 180° arc, giving it the widest possible swing to add mass to the chisel-point on impact. Far more deadly than a simple chopping action, but in the past they haven't been able to use the axe to maximum effect. Will they get the chance in Mayhem?

Bulldog Breed III

Cannock

Weight	97kg
Length	1m
Width	0.7m
Height	0.3m

Speed

15 mph

Turning Circle

0

Clearance

10mm

Power

2 x wheelchair motors

Weapons

Upgraded front flipper and new twin rear-mounted tempered-steel spikes

Armour

Aluminium and titanium shell

Team

Tony Somerfield (Captain), Robert Somerfield and Karla Asplin

Team Battle History

SERIES 3 As Bulldog Breed. Robopig showed no respect for the Bulldog Breed when they shunted them into Shunt, who gave the Bulldog a taste of his axe. Bulldog fought their way clear, but Robopig gave them the same treatment all over again, winning the bout with more than a little help from Shunt

SERIES 4 As Bulldog Breed II. Showed no mercy to Bigger Brother in their heat when Bigger Brother suffered weapons failure. Bulldog flipped them to win. Took on Stinger in the Heat Final. Stinger ripped open Bulldog Breed's armour in a massive attack and then disabled their flipping arm before Bulldog Breed could use it to any real effect

Notes

Smarting from having their armour cleaved open by Stinger, Bulldog Breed's bodywork has been beefed up for better protection in Robot Wars Extreme, but the robot retains its patriotic Union Jack colour scheme. The wedge shape and strengthened flipper mean that the team's battle strategy will remain unchanged – ram and flip – but they do now have an extra sting in their tail

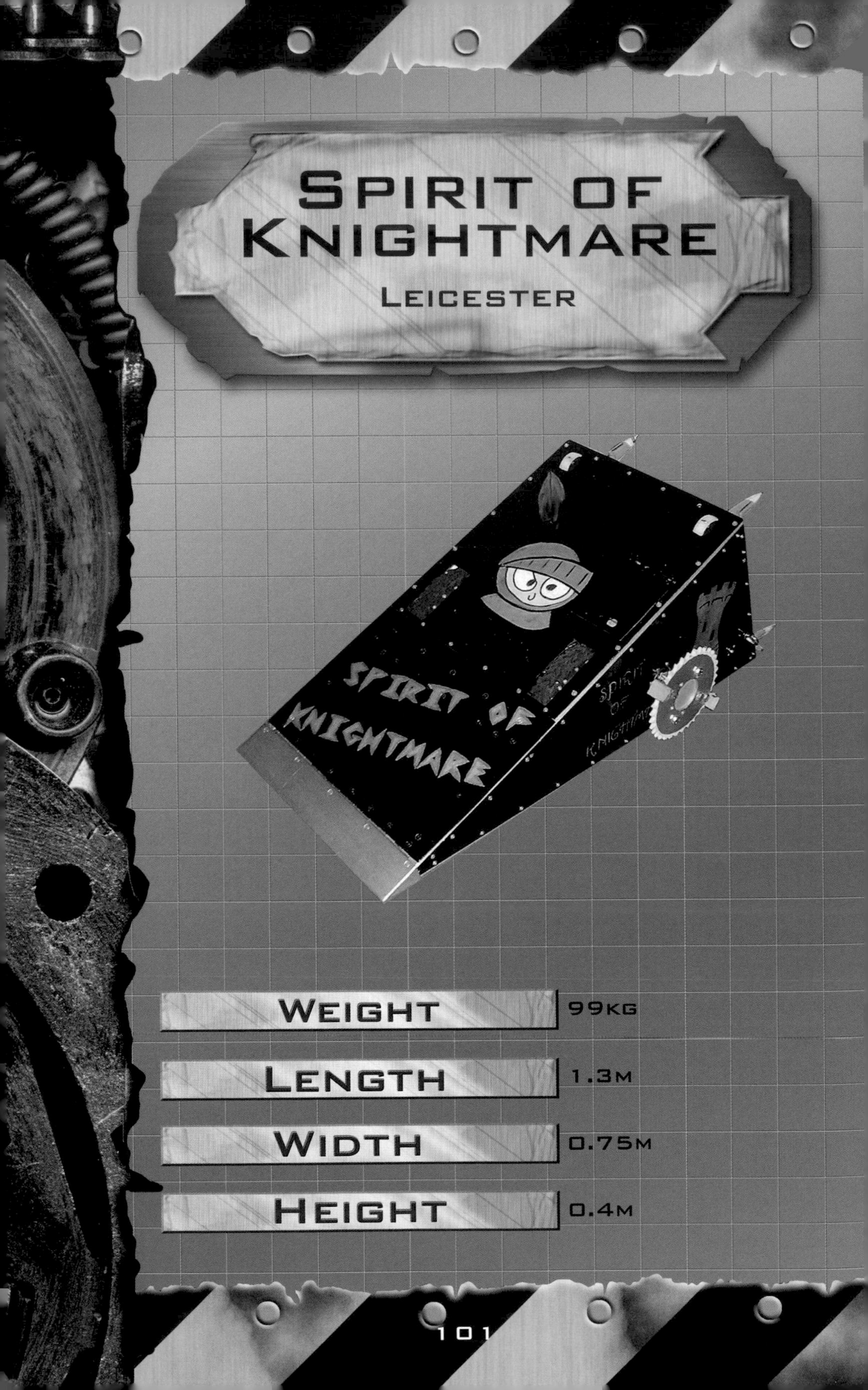

Spirit of Knightmare

Leicester

Weight	99kg
Length	1.3m
Width	0.75m
Height	0.4m

Speed

8.5 mph

Turning Circle

0

Clearance

15mm

Power

2 x 750-watt Bosch electric motors

Weapons

Twin 2000 rpm circular saws, four ramming spikes, twin pneumatic piercers, pneumatic flipper

Armour

Shell made from a road sign

Team

Nigel Paget (Captain), Malcolm Summers and Lee Summers

Team Battle History

SERIES 4 As Knightmare. In a vicious attack, Knightmare locked on to Plunderbird 4 and careered around the arena with them before flipping them into the pit to win the heat. Unfortunately, they didn't fare so well in the Heat Final, when they were rammed to a stand-still by Spawn of Scutter (now Spawn Again) and then shunted into Shunt

Notes

An amazing array of lethal weapons and the ability to run upside down makes Spirit of Knightmare a real threat in the arena. Totally rebuilt with only the motors and electrics surviving from Knightmare, the twin 'blender' saws are awesome in operation. The flipper can lift 80kg, but will that be enough now that the robot weights are all closer to 100kg?

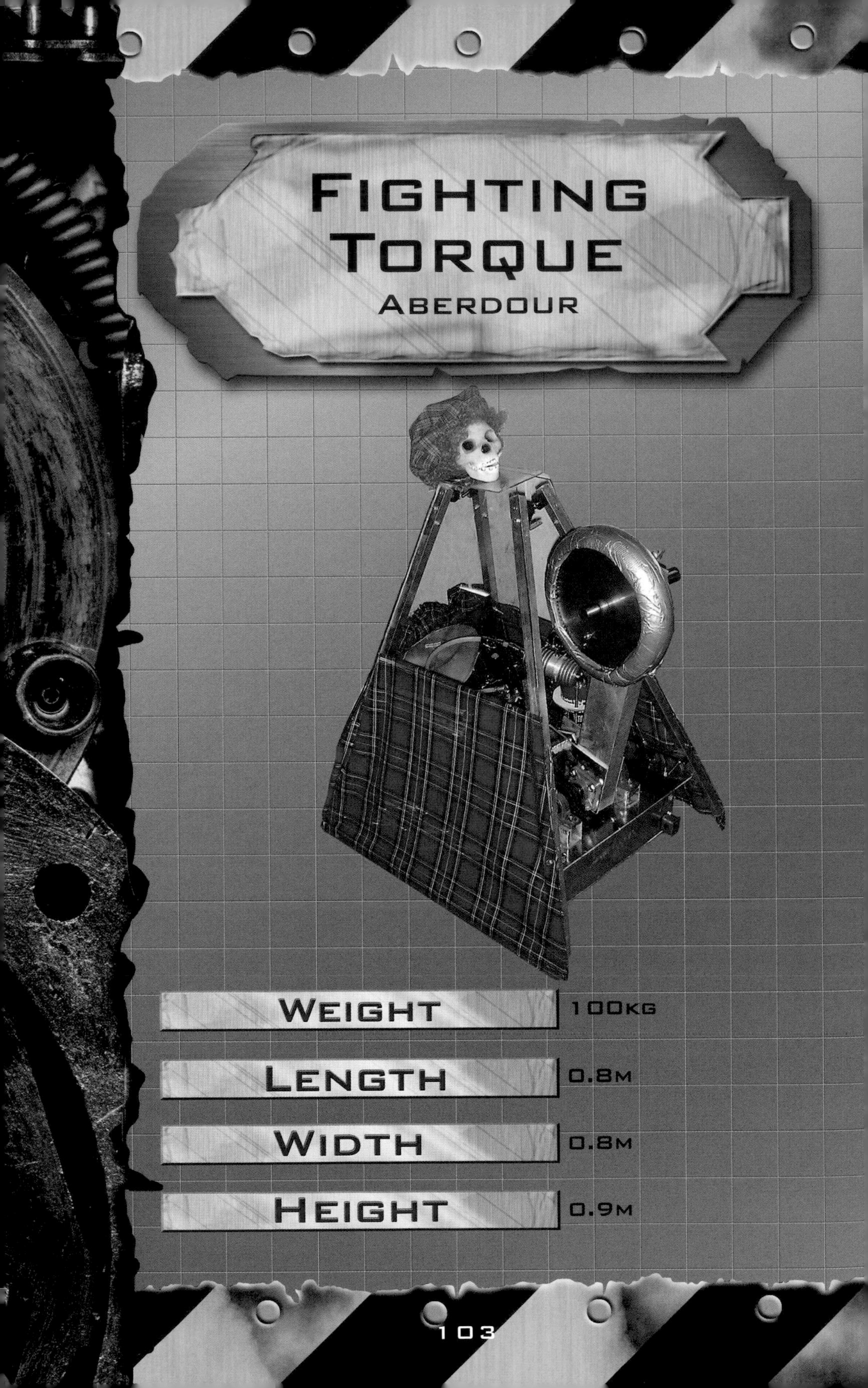

Fighting Torque

Aberdour

Weight	100kg
Length	0.8m
Width	0.8m
Height	0.9m

Speed

16 mph

Turning Circle

0

Clearance

10mm

Power

2 x 500-watt electric motors

Weapons

Crushing arms and devastating axe with 10kg spinning disc axe head

Armour

6mm aluminium plate

Team

Richie McBride (Captain) and Alex McBride

Team Battle History

SERIES 2 As All Torque. Despite being set alight in the Gauntlet trial, All Torque went on to defeat Prometheus by pushing them into the pit, but were totalled by King Buxton (now King B Powerworks) in Heat Final with assistance from Sir Killalot

SERIES 3 As All Torque II. Repeatedly rammed and battered Crippler to win their heat. In a fast and furious Heat Final, Thing II shunted All Torque into Sgt Bash, but it was Shunt's axe that did the real damage. Thunderous blows from Shunt crippled All Torque's receiver and they were dead in the water

SERIES 4 As Small Torque. Shunted Eric in their heat and brought their blade into action, but were flipped by Eric and ended up losing, belching smoke

Notes

A veteran of three Robot Wars, the Torque team embarks on its Robot Wars Extreme campaign with a new attitude, reflected in their new name and impressive new weaponry. Crushing arms powered by a winch motor and a pneumatic axe that strikes with a mocking whoopee cushion noise mean that when Fighting Torque gets hold of you, you know you're in trouble

Wild Card Warriors

How many of you have sat at home watching Robot Wars and seen some total wally drive his robot straight into the pit? How many of you have sat at home and seen a beautifully constructed high-tech robot torn apart by a thug bot with a big axe? And what do you immediately think? You think that some people haven't got a clue about how to win on Robot Wars. But do you?

Wild Card Warriors gives those couch-potato competitors brave enough (or stupid enough) – who have an untried robot at home – the chance to put up or shut up. Newcomers who have never fought in the arena before will be invited to take on some of the top All-Star veterans in head-to-head contests. Those novice robots and teams lucky – or unlucky – enough to be given a Wild Card will get their chance to see what it's really like to do battle in the arena. Will they have the metal to match the mouth and give the veterans a hard time – or will they become metal mincemeat?

The People's Challenge

There have been some epic battles during Robot Wars over the years and most of the veteran robots and teams have come to know each other's strategies and weaponry through getting up close and personal in the arena. There remain some All-Star and veteran robots, however, who have yet to come face-to-face on the arena floor. Chaos II, for example, has never fought Mortis and Razer has never got to grips with Hypno-Disc.

Every Robot Wars fan has probably dreamed about a classic match that they would love to see. Well, a new feature of Robot Wars Extreme will allow those dreams to become reality. The People's Challenge gives you the chance to pit your favourite warriors against each other by voting via the Internet for the fight you would most like to see ... the one battle that you've never seen before.

Potential matches will be discussed on the Web and on the show, and when the suggested matches have been narrowed down to the most popular or intriguing contest, the robots in question will find themselves face-to-face in the arena for The People's Challenge!

The Challenge Belt

Robot Wars Extreme also introduces The Challenge Belt. A competitor of outstanding merit will be awarded The Challenge Belt at the outset of Robot Wars Extreme, but thereafter must defend the belt against opponents who have proved their right to demand a shot at the title of Challenge Champion.

There are three ways an opponent can stake their claim to a Challenge Belt title fight:
1. Showing they are worthy by building up a number of successive victories in the arena
2. Significantly improving on their position in the world rankings
3. Demonstrate in some other significant way that they have earned the right to make the challenge

Equally, the holder of the Challenge Champion title, must be prepared to mount a defence of their title against a challenge that is deemed valid by the International Robot Wars Association.

With the Challenge Belt and the Champion's honour at stake, every challenge match is sure to be a ferocious fight to the death!

Vengence is Mine!

Robot Wars has grown more and more competitive with each passing war. The spirit of camaraderie once shared by the roboteers has become strained over time. Particularly with those teams who've been on the losing side of a Judges' Decision and feel they've been cheated. When the heat is on and the tension high, roboteers have been known to lose their cool.

Why hurl insults, though, when you can hurl each other? If the atmosphere in the pits is starting to get really nasty, it could be time to clear the air with a vengeance match!

The vengeance match is a completely new contest being introduced for Robot Wars Extreme. Robots or teams harbouring grievances, or those whose pride has been wounded as much as their robot armour, can challenge each other to a vengeance match. If it's agreed that there is a score to settle, the opposing teams will be offered the opportunity to do so in the arena . . . and we will have the opportunity to watch a grudge match fought with the sort of passion and commitment that comes straight from the heart. But be prepared, it's gonna get ugly!

Ant Weight

Ant Weight robots are a special new category of fighting machine being introduced for the first time on Robot Wars Extreme. And these mean machines really are extreme – extremely small that is!

Normal competitors in Robot Wars have a 100kg weight limit imposed on them. The Ant Weight versions are limited to just 150 grams! And whilst the Ant Weights can come in a variety of unusual shapes, their overall size is limited in that they must be capable of fitting inside a cube just 10cm square!

Ant Weight roboteers (actually they're normal size, it's just the robots that are teeny) have been training hard for their first appearance on Robot Wars. In the UK alone there are estimated to be around eighty Ant Weight robots and between thirty and forty teams. The six that are featured on Robot Wars Extreme are among the best in the world.

Ant Weights are armed with a variety of weapons, just like the bigger bots, but are so small that they would get lost in the arena and so they do battle in their own mini-arena. The main tactic is to try to shunt your opponent off the mini-arena platform, which ends the game. For Robot Wars Extreme, there will be Mayhem-style bouts with the last one left in the mini-arena declared Ant Weight Champion.

Ant Weight Competitors

ANTO

Newbury

Armed with a formidable flipper, Anto is one of the strongest Ant Weights around and is considered by many as favourite to win the Championship.

Team – Craig Danby (Captain), Derek Danby and Chris Danby

CLOSE SHAVE

Doncaster

This team has built an army of Ant Weights and brought their strongest warrior to Robot Wars Extreme. The crushing arm can cleave straight through other Ant Weights

Team – Alan Parkin (Captain) and Ben Camery

COMBAT ANT

Aylesbury

As well as its bulldozer blade, Combat Ant is armed with a 29,000 rpm spinning cutter powered by a model helicopter motor. Not to be trifled with

Team – Peter Waller (Captain)

LEGION

Leeds

Unbelievably, an Ant Weight cluster bot! Most Ants have very little armour, Legion has none at all to save on weight. Each cluster unit is armed with a flipper

Team – Richard Thompson (Captain) and Alex Timiney

LITTLE NIPPER

Gosport

Don't be detracted by the cutesy name, Little Nipper has some seriously aggressive battle tactics and once they grab hold of another Ant Weight, their opponent can kiss the mini-arena goodbye!

Team – Robert Fitzsimmons (Captain), David Fitzsimmons and Dean Pollard

PANTS

West Sussex

A sophisticated Ant Weight, Pants can be armed with either a scoop or an axe and the arm can be used for self-righting should it ever be flipped over, although it can also run either way up

Team – Peter Collier (Captain)

THE WORLD CHAMIONSHIP

The first World Championships, held after The Third Wars, were organized along slightly different lines from the latest event. The one-on-one elimination battles of the first Championship have been replaced by four heats to be fought Mayhem-style, with four robots battling it out in the ring together. These four adrenaline-charged, action-packed spectaculars will each produce just one winner – either the last man standing or the combatant the judges feel put up the best performance.

The four heat winners will then go on to the Semi-Finals. There will be two Semi-Final matches and two robots will go head-to-head in each Semi. The winner from each Semi-Final will then go through to the Final where the two toughest robo-warriors in the world will battle it out for the title of World Champion.

The UK battlebots are strongly represented by Chaos II, Firestorm III, Tornado and, of course, the reigning World and International Champion, Razer. Razer beat Behemoth on a judges' decision after a titanic battle in the Final of the last World Championship, but will two UK robots make it all the way through to the Final again?

Battle Board

Heat 1

Chaos II – Great Britain
Manta – USA
Mastiff – Italy
Ansgar – Germany

Heat 2

Drillzilla – USA
Neat Machine – Netherlands
Firestorm III – Great Britain
W70 – Sweden

Heat 3

Razer – Great Britain
Diótóir – Ireland
The Revolutionist – USA
Flensburger Power – Germany

Heat 4

Panzer Mk II – USA
Tornado – Great Britain
Philliper – Belgium
Yeborobo – South Africa

Drillzilla
California, USA

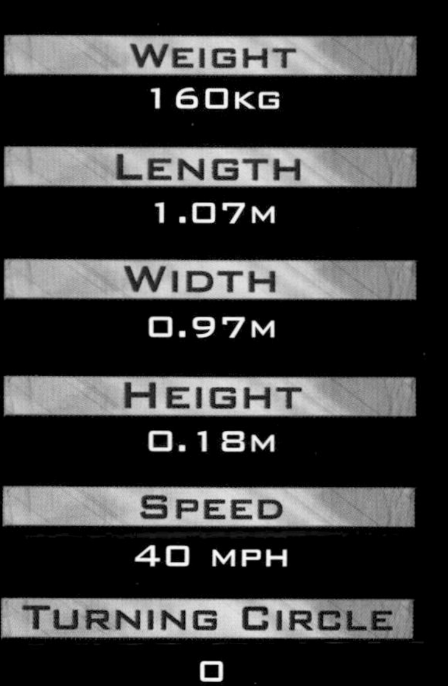

Weight
160kg

Length
1.07m

Width
0.97m

Height
0.18m

Speed
40 mph

Turning Circle
0

Clearance
15mm

Power
4 x 20 horsepower electric motors driving two banks of feet

Weapons
Three razor-sharp piercing teeth mounted on a drill, plus steel jaws for grasping

Team
Dave Hall (Captain), Bruce Hall and Chris Kallai

Notes A 'walker' robot capable of incredible speed and which makes an incredible amount of noise! The eight feet on each side are well protected, which means this one is likely to stay mobile and maintain a dangerous level of activity

The Revolutionist

Virginia, USA

Weight
94kg

Length
0.7m

Width
0.7m

Height
0.19m

Speed
10 – 15 mph

Turning Circle
0

Clearance
38mm

Power
Power 4 x 6v electric motors

Weapons
Electric-powered spinning cutter with two steel teeth

Team
Brian Nave (Captain), Rebecca Nave and Michael Nave

Notes
This monster has a 25mm – thick chassis that makes it incredibly tough. It has been driven into a concrete wall at full speed and suffered no damage

Manta
Virginia, USA

Weight
84kg

Length
1.12m

Width
0.95m

Height
0.32m

Speed
20 mph

Turning Circle
0

Clearance
10mm

Power
24v electric motors driving all six wheels

Weapons
Rear-mounted Carbide ramming point and front mounted spinning steel blade/hammer

Team
Jeff Cesnik (Captain), Billy Boden and Chris Tyson

Notes A well armed and fast machine, difficult to stop with its six-wheel drive and best to avoid if you don't want to be hit with that evil ramming spike

Panzer Mk II
California, USA

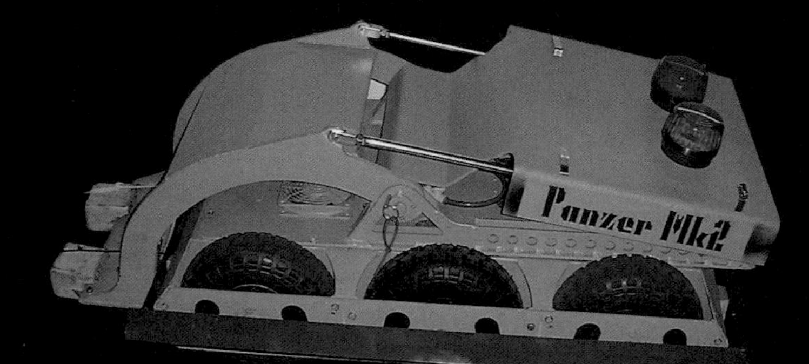

Weight
99kg

Length
1.22m

Width
0.75m

Height
0.45m

Speed
10 mph

Turning Circle
0

Clearance
12mm

Power
24v electric motors driving all six wheels

Weapons
Interchangeable weapons options include spinning cutter disc

Team
Don Lariviére (Captain), Todd Mendenhall and Jennifer Twisdom

Notes Its six wheels will make this powerful weapons platform difficult to immobilize. One of its weapons options is a lifter capable of flipping an impressive 130kg

ANSGAR
GERMANY

WEIGHT
72KG

LENGTH
1M

WIDTH
1M

HEIGHT
1M

SPEED
12 MPH

TURNING CIRCLE
0

CLEARANCE
0-5MM

POWER
12V ELECTRIC CAR-WINDOW MOTOR

WEAPONS
FLIPPING LEVER AND THRUSTING LANCE

TEAM
JOACHIM THOMSEN (CAPTAIN), SUNGE THOMSEN AND SASCHA THOMSEN

NOTES CAN 'SIT DOWN' TO AVOID BEING SHUNTED. WEAPONS OPERATE AT HIGH REPEAT STRIKE RATE OF UP TO 300 TIMES PER MINUTE

Flensburger Power

Germany

Weight
91kg

Length
1m

Width
0.5m

Height
0.3m

Speed
5 – 6 mph

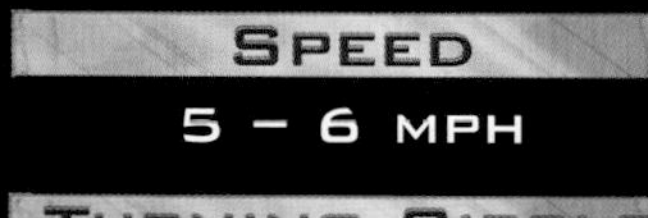

Turning Circle
0

Clearance
7mm

Power
12v electric windscreen-wiper motor

Weapons
2 spinning cutter discs and a thrusting spear

Team
Michael Snoor (Captain), Anita Jessen and Andre Bruske

Notes
Flensburger's weapons may not look like the most fearsome in the Championship, but it does have entertaining light and sound effects

Mastiff

Italy

Weight
85kg

Length
0.83m

Width
1.13m

Height
0.65m

Speed
10 mph

Turning Circle
0

Clearance
10mm

Power
12v electric motor

Weapons
Reinforced for shunting, wth a pneumatic lifter for tipping and flipping

Team
Tiziano Rovella (Captain), Gabriella Formica and Luca Rovella

Notes A classic wedge-shaped robot, whose battle strategy is clearly to get underneath an opponent and use its only weapon, the pneumatic lifter

W70

Sweden

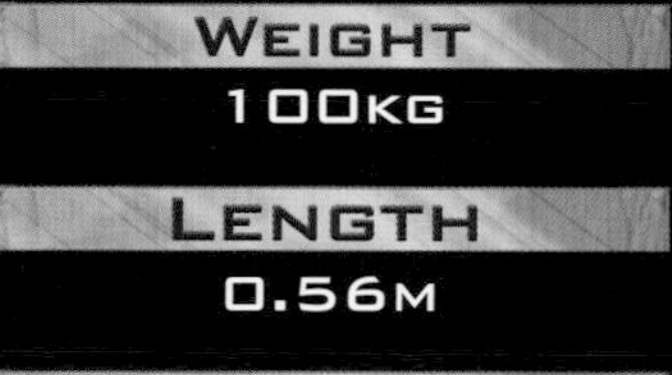

Weight
100kg

Length
0.56m

Width
0.69m

Height
0.34m

Speed
3 mph

Turning Circle
0

Clearance
15mm

Power
12v electric motor

Weapons
Whirling weapons platform can have attachments, including blades, hooks, flails

Team
Janis Platbardis (Captain), Christer Floors and Mats Larsen

Notes Defence appears to be the best form of attack with this former swimming pool cleaner. It's too slow to chase anyone, so it waits for them to come in close and then starts spinning

Yeborobo
South Africa

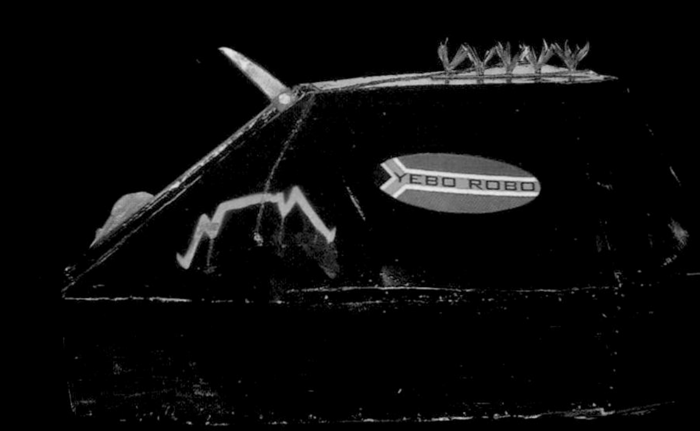

Weight
92kg

Length
1.2m

Width
0.8m

Height
0.45m

Speed
3 mph

Turning Circle
1–2m

Clearance
30mm

Power
12v truck windscreen-wiper motor

Weapons
Razor-sharp pick axe and conveyor lifter device

Team
Andrew Kerr (Captain), Michael Kerr and Jon Kerr

Notes A highly manoeuvrable three-wheeled combatant, which will cause the others plenty of problems if it can get in close with that pick axe

Philipper

Belgium

Weight
99.9kg

Length
1.4m

Width
0.7m

Height
0.6m

Speed
8 mph

Turning Circle
0

Clearance
10mm

Power
24v electric motor

Weapons
Lifting and flipping blades mounted front and rear

Team
Phillippe Poppe (Captain), Nancy Poppe and Sam Poppe

Notes Designed to look like a dolphin (and named partly in honour of the famous dolphin TV star Flipper) this robot's main tactic is to flip its opponents

Neat Machine
Netherlands

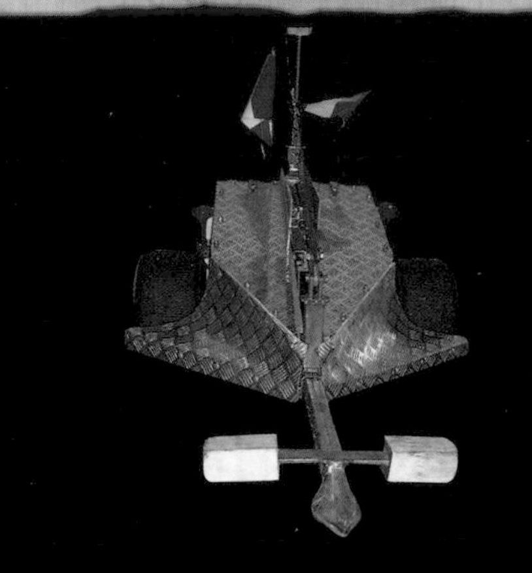

Weight
100kg

Length
1.5m

Width
1.1m

Height
0.8m

Speed
15 mph

Turning Circle
0

Clearance
20mm

Power
24v electric wheel-chair motor

Weapons
Pick axe for chopping and axle-mounted double-edged spears

Team
Arthur Van Uift (Captain), Wouter Van Den Ende and Jur Breuring

Notes Horns sound when the pick axe is activated and the machine can spin at a rate of 150 times per minute to bring those axle spears into play

INDEX

ROBOT WARS™
EXTREME™